The People of Wheelbarrow Lane

by the same author

THE LAND AND LIFE OF CHINA
CHINA THROUGH A COLLEGE WINDOW
STRANGE HARMONY (a record of internment)
(Edinburgh House Press)

I STAYED IN CHINA
(George Allen & Unwin Ltd)

Extracts from reviews of *I Stayed in China*

'Deep affection for the Chinese, a nice sense of humour . . . His book is beautifully written.' H. D. Ziman in the *Telegraph*.

'One could not ask for more sensitive portraits than these.' *Times*

'The Chinese people stand out as tremendously real . . . The book is the most touching, the most moving, and the most true of all the books written about China since the Second World War.' Dr. Joseph Needham in the *Guardian*

'Its special quality lies in the sensitive portraits of the author's Chinese friends and the occasional flashes of dialogue and Chinese sayings.' *Times Educational Supplement*

'The book has vividness, charm and charity.' *New Statesman*

The People of Wheelbarrow Lane

William G. Sewell

with illustrations by Yü Tse-tan

London
George Allen & Unwin Ltd
RUSKIN HOUSE · MUSEUM STREET

ISBN 0 04 951017 7

Printed in Great Britain
in 12 on 13 point Bembo type
by Jolly & Barber Limited,
Rugby

In gratitude to Yü Tse-tan
language teacher and artist
also in remembrance of
the People of Wheelbarrow Lane

These scenes from the lives of a small number of people during pre-liberation days in West China are mostly autobiographical, frequently synthetic, but always as authentic as the author can make them, his memory helped by diaries and letters which he himself wrote. Names have all been changed, except that of the artist, with whom some harmless liberties have been taken, among them, moving his home into Wheelbarrow Lane. The author alone is responsible for this account, but he wishes most sincerely to thank Ormerod Greenwood for his generous encouragement and advice, also Liao Hung-Ying and Derek Bryan who have made valuable comments.

Contents

I

Wheelbarrow Lane

WHEN I OPENED THE DOOR he was standing on the verandah steps, dressed in a long blue gown, a black round brimless hat upon his head. From his appearance he might have been any one of the great multitude of artisans. Although, like most Chinese of his age, he was beardless, from each nostril there sprouted a tuft of black hair. It was these tufts that attracted my attention. Nervously he was twisting one of them with his fingers, but, as I approached him, he politely withdrew his hand from his face, and bowing, handed me a letter which he held with both hands.

As I looked at the envelope he resumed the twisting, betraying his anxiety, although his face remained quite passive. The note inside was brief, written in a round girlish hand. 'Rumour says you want a cook. I hope this is true, for you might like to try the bearer, Fu Lu-chin. He has been a god-send while our own cook has been back to his home. Now Fu needs a job – western or Chinese style.' The signature was in even larger letters: 'Molly Wu.'

We did indeed need a cook; and Fu Lu-chin not only became ours on trial, but remained with us. He knew his job, kept our household machine running smoothly, and clearly knew how to deal with big-nosed barbarians like Mary and myself. Our small daughter soon adored him, following him around, repeating Chinese words after him and soon teaching him a little English, although when he first arrived she

was too young to do more than lisp *yao* and *bu-yao* – want and
not-want – those basic essentials needed to enable any child or
foreigner to survive in the China of those days.

Fu Lu-chin kept our mutual interests well served for almost
a decade, during the heyday of the Kuomintang, before the
Japanese, at Pearl Harbour, brought the world crashing about
our ears. He was there in the background, yet this story of our
friends rightly begins with him because he was the means of
bringing Molly Wu into our lives. Until we knew her our
interests were almost entirely divided between students and
teacher colleagues on the one hand, and personal servants on
the other. The former were beginning to break with Chinese
tradition and were turning to the new thought which they
believed might make their weakened country great once
more; while the latter were chiefly concerned with trying to
conform to the strange life demanded of them by their
western employers. The *lao-beh-hsin*, old hundred names, the
man in the street, our near neighbours in Wheelbarrow Lane,
were to us little more than animated puppets, moving
quaintly across an unfamiliar scene. Our friendship with
Molly transformed them into living men and women.

There was considerable gossip about Molly, who had the
reputation of holding herself aloof from those of us connected
with Jen Dah, the Privately Established University of
Benevolence and Justice, where I taught chemistry in Chinese
which was adequate, but far from perfect. Molly was an
English girl married to a Chinese, the natural object of
curiosity and, with some of the older westerners and Chinese,
of disapproval. Mary and I knew that she must have already

---

[1] Se Li Jen Ni Dah Shioh, to give it its full romanised Chinese name, had been started as a
Christian venture at Duliang in the far west of China. It was opened by a number of
missionary societies soon after the overthrow of the Imperial Dragon Throne in the days of
Sun Yat Sen, when China first became a republic. As time went on, especially after Chiang
Kai-shek and the Kuomintang gained power, the Chinese Ministry of Education exerted
increasing control, although the final authority still remained with the founding members
in New York and London.

been in Duliang for a year or more; and having recently
returned from our leave, we were anxious to meet her. Now
we were able to take the opportunity of thanking her personally for sending us our new cook, Fu.

Molly lived in one of the larger houses at the far end of
Wheelbarrow Lane, quite near the sharp turn into the main
road to the city gate. The Lane led from there for about a
quarter of a mile up a slight slope to the main gate of the
university, after which it degenerated into little more than a
track between rice fields. We spoke of it in English as a lane,
but the Chinese word could more truthfully be translated
alley. In those days it was nothing more than a ribbon of
uneven paving stones, down the centre of which grooves
had been worn by the iron-clad wheels of the heavy wheel-
barrows trundled along throughout decades if not centuries.
The stones were flanked on either side by hard ruts of dried
blackened mud, or dark green slime when it was wet. An
open drain along one side, covered in some places by flag-
stones, was convenient but stinking. The Lane and the houses
along both sides were in striking contrast to Jen Dah itself,
with its spacious grounds, broad gravelled walks, and magnificent buildings with western-style interiors, but decorated
with turned-up Chinese roofs and tiled eyebrows, shading
windows.

The Lane houses near the university were very poor
indeed. First came a long, one storey, mud building, divided
into ten or more rooms, each large enough to hold bed-
boards and table. These were the homes of some of our daily
labourers. The long roof was poorly thatched with corn
stalks and pampas grass cut from the graveland near by. There
were no windows to pierce the adobe walls, the only light
coming through the shuttered doorways.

Further on, opposite a small temple, whose dusty tutelary
gods looked down upon a private school, the houses were
better, built of bamboo lath and plaster squares, framed in

timber which was either plain or painted red. These were small shops as well as dwellings. Then came larger shops, their increased prosperity made known by the black lacquered beams and the hanging signs with characters in gold. They were open to the Lane, and it was from these that our servants bought our daily food, the vegetables and fish, the meat and rice. It was here that Deng the carpenter, who did odd jobs for us, had his shop. Usually he greeted us, but that morning as we passed he was busy shouting orders to his men above the noise of sawing. Beyond were the tinsmith, a tailor, the coffin shop and bucket maker, the rice bowl seller; and everywhere there were people. Men and women talked as they worked or idled, children swarmed about them, dogs fought and apprentices snatched time off to watch what it was all about.

A small open space was once a playground, called by those with long memories Hercules Park, after a down-river Christian pastor, Hercules Woo, who had practical gifts and reclaimed the land for children to play on; but Hercules had been killed in an accident and the playground become derelict. Now it was used by some dyers who spread their long lines of narrow cotton cloth on the ground for bleaching or to darken after steeping in the indigo vats. Conveniently it was opposite the tea-shop, the Lane's social centre, from which the workmen could watch over their cloth while sipping tea.

A little beyond the playground turned dyer's yard was a black lacquered door leading to Jen Hsiao, the Primary School linked to the university. Gow Chung-ho, the headmaster, was coming out as we passed, accompanied by Old Teacher Ma, the head of the university Chinese Department. Gow bowed to us, but the full-bearded Ma, an old Chinese scholar with conventional manners, not only bowed but raised his large round spectacles in politeness even if, as we suspected, he could feel no real respect for barbarians. He was dressed in a long black silk gown and short satin jacket, while Gow, a middle-aged man with scanty beard, was in homely western-style clothes. Gow was unofficial guardian of the Lane, the settler of disputes. Often he could be found in the tea-shop, listening to noisy argument, calming quarrelling neighbours, encouraging warm compromise which often brought peace and happiness, where cold justice would have left a heritage of rancour.

Further along, beyond the black lacquered door of the school was the *Kuai-lo kei-dien*, the Inn of Peace and Quiet, with its noisy untidy yard, where unfortunate guests who had to spend a night found not *kuai-lo* but bugs and fleas in plenty. The loud voiced proprietor Liu was fat and greasy, but pleasant enough when money was in sight.

On the other side of the Lane, opposite the inn and comfortably near the tea-shop, was a very public convenience. In the dimly understood interests of hygiene the outside walls had been whitewashed, although the interior remained untouched. The front wall, with two openings, had only recently been built. One entrance invitingly announced in Chinese characters: Eastern Pool; while the other gave an alternative choice: Western Lake. Between them, perhaps the far reaching effects of Jen Dah education, were the untruthful but large letters: W.C. Both gates, in fact, led to the same stinking pit, covered precariously with open stalls, which had been unchanged for as long as anyone living in the Lane could remember. Instinctively those not forced to tarry there would quicken steps as they passed along, especially on hot humid days when smells hung heavy.

At the more affluent end of the Lane there were alley-ways on either side leading to houses which were quite pretentious, though not so old or spacious as some of the residences within the city walls. To look across Duliang is to see endless grey tile roofs, made gay by the green tops of trees growing from countless heavenly wells, the courtyards around which the people live. Every city street seems always to be thronged with swarming multitudes; and as the westerner threads his way among the slowly moving crowds he cannot at times escape a wave of apprehension at his own utter insignificance. In the suburbs, however, the streets are usually less crowded, and that morning as we went to thank Molly Wu it was neither smells nor people that we heeded. It was one of those rare days, after rain, when we could see the towering snow-clad Minya Konka and other mountains, a hundred miles away, near the frontier of eastern Tibet. They were rooted in mists, their peaks rising clear and sharp against the deep blue sky, their whiteness still seeming to have a touch of pink, although the dawn was long since past.

Our thoughts, like our eyes, were raised to those distant hills beyond the lower end of Wheelbarrow Lane so that we missed, and had to return to, the narrow passage between a wine shop and a tailor's. Although too insignificant to attract the attention of a casual passer-by it led to a large Chinese house, hidden behind the frontage of shops. Our

approach produced noisy barking from the dogs, which
dashed out, neck hair bristling and fangs showing, to
protect their home. Having learnt caution we stood still
while several women, roused by the alarm, came to the
door and with curses and threats persuaded the dogs to draw
back. 'Guests, western guests,' they shouted above the
clamour; and the cry was echoed inside the gates.

Western guests could only be for one person; and before
long Molly was with the women greeting us. Tall and
slender, she stood out among them, different in so many
ways. Her hair, light brown and wavy was conspicuous
above the cluster of straight black hair. All the Chinese
women were shorter than she was; their black trousers and
white jackets made Molly still more outstanding in pink
blouse and pale blue skirt. Her eyes seemed palest green
among the deep brown ones, which all were turned towards
us. 'Come in, please come in,' she called in Chinese, and then
laughingly repeated her words in English as she led us round
the screen into the courtyard. In every room around it
people lived; many were sitting at their open doors, some,
with their bamboo wheels turning, were spinning cotton, all
talking and laughing with each other. There was a hush as
they paused to look at us, and then chattering broke out once
more.

Through a passage beside the large room at the back,
facing the main door from which it was protected by the
spirit screen inside the entrance, we went into the second
courtyard. This had never been completed; although there
were rooms at each side, the back was open, and revealed a
lath and plaster house, which boasted two storeys, and was
built on an enclosed piece of ground.

'My home,' Molly held the door for us to enter. 'We are
lucky to have this place of our own, instead of living with
crowds of people around a courtyard.'

Like other lath and plaster houses no exact plan could have

been made until the building was complete, as the final shape depended on the natural curves of the tree trunks used as main beams. In the living room the curtains hung slightly away from the walls, as in a ship unable to right itself after a roll. There was a decided downhill walk to the kitchen; and the plaster squares were not all true. At first encounter one felt slightly dizzy, the feeling increased by the brightly coloured cushions and curtains.

The courtyards, or heavenly wells, of Chinese houses are cool in summer, but often airless and very noisy. Frequently they are paved, with paths around the square, while in the centre flowering shrubs are grown in raised troughs or urns. Around Molly's house the open space had been turned into a western style garden, with flowers and shrubs growing in the ground itself. From a seat in the window it was possible to look across it into the uncompleted courtyard in which grew two osmanthus trees. There were already some tiny pale-yellow blossoms among the leaves, their delicate fragrance, borne on a slight breeze, refreshed the air.

Molly was shy and restrained at first as we talked over the bowls of tea her woman servant, the *da-niang*, had brought as soon as we arrived. We gave her our small gifts of fruit and flowers, talking of Fu and then about each other. Pleasant coincidences occur in life: we three westerners meeting together for the first time in the far interior of China discovered we had all lived quite near each other in north England. In happiness, so much the greater because of the distance from our homeland, we were drawn together, and a friendship formed which was to remain unbroken. 'I never believed I should like anyone at Jen Dah,' Molly confided, and soon was telling us the reason. At Brightmoor, in industrial Yorkshire, where she was born, she had met and married Wu Deh-min, a student. There had been no clouds to dim her happiness until on the ship sailing eastward they had both been made to feel inferior and socially excluded.

Three matrons returning to India, who had been looking for a fourth to join them at bridge, snubbed her when she offered to play. Also some old hands from the Far East presumed that because she was married to a Chinese she would welcome their attentions with relief. Once she heard: 'She was his landlady's daughter – seduced, I expect.' Conversations would suddenly die away as she approached. The confidence with which she had left home began to be slightly undermined, although at first she refused to admit it.

Among the passengers was an elderly missionary couple, whom she enjoyed as they told her stories of their life in China. The Reverend John Harlass, tall and thin, clean shaven, hollow cheeked, had eyes of blue which possessed that far-away look which Molly told us she had come to associate with people who had spent long years in China. His wife seemed joyless, any gaiety she may have possessed having vanished with her youth. They needed human warmth to soften the cold charity of their austere lives. Molly had longed to share with them some of her own great joy in life.

In time the stories had become more pointed, and one day when she was alone Harlass drew an empty deck-chair close to hers. 'I should do more to prepare you about China,' he told her, 'for I am sure your charming husband could never have warned you; and if you do not know you will be unable to adjust yourself.' He spoke of cruelty and deception, of the power of the family council. 'China is the land of buried hopes, lost faith and dead ambitions,' he said in words which she remembered, because she later found that for so many westerners they were true. 'It is a country which deals hardly, brings to nothing your best endeavours. It is like a great cliff. The seas of our restless western civilization beat upon it, but long after the waves have receded the cliff remains unchanged – perhaps scarred in places, perhaps a little ferro-concrete on its surface, an electric wire or two, but essentially the same.'

Molly defended the land of her adoption, seeing it through the eyes of love, yet struck with a little fear, because she realised that he had experience, whereas she, in truth, had none. 'That is not what my husband tells me,' she had said. 'Of course China got left behind and now has to catch up; but she is learning quickly, building on those old foundations which are so great and wonderful.'

But the missionary told her, truthfully she now recognized, that he knew more of China than she did and there was something lacking in the people's character. 'Education perhaps,' Molly suggested. 'No, Christ,' Harlass said. 'Without him they are adrift, a ship without a helmsman.'

In the face of such conviction, although she was beginning to feel uncomfortable, Molly said no more. Then, as if by pre-arranged plan, Mrs Harlass appeared and took her husband's place. She told her how they both felt responsibility towards her, a young girl going to China unprotected.

'But I am not alone. I have a husband,' Molly protested, beginning to feel angry.

Mrs Harlass shook her head. 'Quite unprotected really,' she insisted. 'No one of experience to advise you. Your mother must be worried, poor soul. But you can rely on me.' And she patted Molly's arm. 'My husband and I have prayed about you. It may be very difficult indeed being married to a Chinese. We shall pray for you.'

Molly told us how she rushed to the boat deck for fresh air. She was not only hurt, but frightened. It was the first time she had wanted to strike another person. She walked up and down, and then stood watching the bows as gently they rose and fell, the ship parting the blue waters in a wave of foam as it pushed its way towards her new home. There was a refreshing breeze and she loosened her brown hair and held up her bare arms until they grew cool. At last she felt clean again. There were enough difficulties in marriages like theirs without adding unnecessary complications; so she and

Deh-min had resolved that in future they would keep clear of missionaries. Although living so near they had no contacts with Jen Dah because they knew it was a Christian university.

She was older now, and not so easily discouraged. She was ready to admit that the Harlesses had truly been anxious for her well-being, and that they belonged to a generation that is passing. We assured her that the British and Americans at Jen Dah certainly had a different outlook and she promised to visit us, if only to talk of Brightmoor and see how Cook Fu was managing.

In response to our enquiries she told us a little about her husband, Deh-min. He was in charge of a model factory attached to the Leather School, outside the West Gate of the city. Their small son, Han-ku, was spending the morning at the nursery school run by the junior school, Jen Hsiao. This, being entirely Chinese, she regarded with more favour than the university, although together with the middle school, Jen Chung, they were linked together to form rungs on an educational ladder.

As Molly led us back through the courtyards to the gate she told us of the people who lived there. They were the family and friends of her landlord Lee, from whom their own house was rented. 'It was long before I knew for certain which was his wife,' Molly was saying as we threaded our way through the women and children, all talkative and friendly. 'I used to think of her as the one who was usually pregnant, but so many of them are.' Indeed most young women, and not only in the poorer portion of the Lane, appeared to have a small child tied on their backs or toddling by their side, one in their arms, held near to ready breasts, and frequently an obvious third as yet unborn.

An older man, wearing wide cotton trousers, and a jacket once white, now beaten grey upon the washing stones, came from one of the rooms to get a glimpse of us. He too was carrying a baby. 'My landlord Lee,' said Molly as we bowed, his face wrinkling into innumerable brown furrows as he smiled. 'He can speak some English,' she added. It was a word of warning as well as of introduction.

'Not really,' he was beaming with pleasure at being able to speak with westerners, while the women near enough to hear nudged each other in their pride for him, 'I was at mission school.' Then when we asked if the children were his he giggled: 'I am very productive.' Molly whispered that she thought he had nine. His eldest girl was working in the leather factory, a personal favour extracted from her husband. Lee pointed to an attractive child, his second daughter, her dark eyes shining in a face too pale. She was feeding a much smaller sister, who was sitting in a plaited bamboo basket like a small bird in a nest mouth open wide, while the elder child held a bowl and deftly with chopsticks shovelled in the rice.

'Little sister, how old are you?' asked Mary.

'Tai-tai, I am fifteen,' she replied.

'And do you go to school?' But in reply to my question she laughed.

'Hsien-sen, how could I go to school? I have so many brothers; they must have first choice.' She accepted her lot without question, without self-pity. In time she would marry and have children of her own.

At last, to a chorus of 'Walk slowly, walk slowly, slowly,' from the women at the gate, we went with Molly down the passage to the Lane. Then from the tailor's shop came a cheerful call: 'Wu Tai-tai, Lady Wu. You have guests. Up so early! Have you eaten breakfast?'

'Yes, yes. I have eaten – and you? These guests are from England. They know the very town in which I lived. Isn't that something wonderful? – and if ever you want a good tailor to make dresses or shirts this is the man,' she added in English.

Tailor Su, as he talked, kept blowing on the charcoal in his iron, with which, when hot enough, he smoothed the jacket he was making, having first made it damp by skilfully squirting over it a mouthful of water. A pair of red trousers, embroidered in white and blue, just completed and folded neatly, were waiting on his hanger until someone seeing them would tell the owner they were ready.

We were examining the dragon's head at the end of the pole, a delight of workmanship, when a voice called to us. 'Hsien-sen, Su-mu, where are you going?' and turning round, we saw the language teacher who had taught us on our first arrival in Duliang. He was threading his way through the little crowd which, inquisitive about foreigners, their strange ways and clothes, was collecting around the tailor's shop. Yü Tse-tan blinked at us with his short-sighted eyes, wrinkling his pale yellow face with a smile of genuine pleasure at the encounter. 'And Wu Tai-tai, up so early?' He bowed to Molly. 'Have you eaten food yet?'

The pleasantries demanded no reply, and far from being early it was nearly noon – high time we were returning home.

'So you also know Mr Yü.' Molly turned to us, but spoke so that he could hear. 'I know he often goes up to your end of the Lane, but I never knew where he went.'

'Our excellent language teacher,' Mary and I spoke together, bowing towards the obviously delighted Yü.

'And the best of students.' Politeness compelled his reply, regardless of our failures, which we ourselves could mention only cursorily, for to stress them would have reflected on his skill as a teacher as much as upon ourselves. We could, however, call heaven to witness that if we, two stupid foreigners, had any ability to speak Chinese it was solely due to his skill and patience.

'I know him only as an artist and a neighbour,' Molly told us. 'He lives over there,' and we looked vaguely at the shops across the Lane, towards which, Chinese fashion, she pointed with her chin.

Teacher Yü walked with us back to Jen Dah. Mary in western style led the way, although any Chinese woman would have walked modestly behind the men-folk. Yü and I progressed more slowly. The paved path down the middle of the Lane was sufficient only for two people to walk abreast or pass each other. As we could not decide who should walk in front, one or other of us had to step off on to the rough earth from time to time, either when the path broke down, or when we were approached by someone whose burden or status gave him right of way. It was the perennial problem, so absorbing to the Chinese, so frustrating to the impatient westerner, of who should give way. Yü, honouring me as a foreign guest in China, insisted that he should yield; but, realizing the respect due to my old teacher, I felt equally sure that I should be the one to take to the ruts. Moreover I had stout leather shoes, whereas he wore soft cloth slippers. We finished up at the Jen Dah gates walking one each side of the empty path.

II

The Artist Entertains

———◇———

A RED ENVELOPE, larger than was usual, was brought to our house a day or two later. Cook Fu himself handed it to us, and stood leisurely twisting one of the tufts in his nostrils as he waited to see what we should make of it. Usually our rather bitter labourer, the *ku-li,* Lao Sung, the odd-job boy, brought in the notes, which, in a world without telephones, were constantly arriving; but this time, doubtless after consultations in the kitchen, it had been decided that the occasion demanded a more formal presentation.

'It's an invitation from your teacher,' Fu told us. But as we extracted the flimsy sheet we ourselves were able to read, for it was written in the clear large simple characters which Yü Tse-tan knew his pupils would understand. We were asked to eat common homely food with him the following evening. 'I shall give the bearer of such good news a little tea-money,' Fu announced as he left us, already feeling under his white apron of office and blue gown for the purse tied safely round his waist.

We knew now that Yü lived at the lower but more affluent end of Wheelbarrow Lane, across the road from the alley-way leading to Landlord Lee's house, but we need not have worried because we did not know the exact place.

There are few secrets in the Lane, everyone delights in other people's business; after all Mrs Yü had herself been shopping, and every shopkeeper she visited, and soon every-

one else, knew that guests were invited to a feast. There were
knowing nods as we walked down the Lane that afternoon,
and children were anxious to show us the way, while Tailor
Su, who had evidently been told to watch for us, dispatched a
child to tell Mr Yü of our approach. Su himself directed us to
a weaver of cotton cloth, who worked nearly opposite his
own shop. We hesitated, as it seemed not at all where we
should go. 'Just that place,' he shouted loudly. 'Right in
through the shop.'

The weaver did not pause casting his shuttle back and
forth, clack-clack, clack-clack, as we entered his shop, and
were directed by the children to a half-hidden doorway at the
back. Passing through it, we found ourselves in front of a
large house.

The promise of the Chinese Revolution of 1911 had never
been fulfilled. The country, instead of becoming unified, had
disintegrated into lawlessness, with local war-lords and

their private armies holding despotic sway. Although
eventually Chiang Kai-shek had been able to unite a considerable part of the country, establishing the Kuomintang or
Nationalist Government, yet there were still parts, such as
this far-away province of Szechwan, where war-lord
governors gave little more than lip service to the distant
Central Government. Local wars were still fought, and it
became the custom to hide the homes of the more well-to-do
behind small shops. They were a protection from lawless
men who might prowl the streets, bands of hungry disorganized soldiers, pressgangs in search of carriers or
recruits, and from beggars who, trading on their loathsome-
ness, would blackmail respectable citizens by crowding
round their doorways, refusing to let people in or out until
they had given money. Also the rents from the shops
brought extra income during times which were becoming
increasingly hard.

Yü Tse-tan was at his doorway to welcome us, descending
the steps from the open lacquered doors so that we could
meet on level ground. He was wearing a shiny black satin
jacket, with patterns for long life and happiness woven in the
damask, over his long gown of grey silk. On his head he had
the usual black round hat, with the conventional button on
top of all – black in his case, red being for the newly married
or those on whom fortune had given a special smile. White
buttons were reserved for those who mourned. Yü was
bowing to us, waving us in, repeating words of welcome
and wiping away the water which so continually dribbled
from his eyes.

With few exceptions, gone were the days when these
larger houses were occupied by one extended family. It was
becoming more rare for several generations actually to live
together, although it remained as an ideal, tenuously
keeping people together in bonds of affection and loyalty.
Few sons were able to bring their brides back to the ancestral

homes. They had to go out to seek their livelihood; and those women who were educated often themselves worked outside the home, putting their husbands before their mothers-in-law, no longer blindly marrying as their elders wished.

Yü led us to the large room at the back of the inner courtyard, but how much of the house he actually owned or rented we never knew. The tenants freely lent each other their rooms and their possessions, and also gave each other help – the price, a carefully adjusted reciprocity. With so many people crowded round the courtyards there was possibility of endless friction: the wonder was not that sometimes there was angry conflict with shrill voices raised in violent denunciations, leading occasionally to suicide yet rarely to blows, but that harmony so usually prevailed. Through long centuries the Chinese had learnt the art of living, with its give and take, and acceptance of the fact that it was wrong to stand in the way of others.

With western insensitivity we had arrived on time, and were obviously too early, although the consternation was politely hidden. A woman servant brought bowls of noodle soup, while the gateman was sent to summon other guests. Soon Molly Wu and her husband arrived; and we realised that Yü Tse-tan had thoughtfully arranged the party to bring us closer together. With an insight so many of our Chinese friends seemed to possess he believed we had much in common and might help each other. Like every Chinese he was at heart a middle-man, an arranger of events.

Molly was dressed in a long silk Chinese gown, fitting closely to her slender figure. It was obviously in the latest fashion, with long slits at either side, which rumour had said was the new custom in far-away Shanghai. She was at least three inches taller than Wu Deh-min, whom now we met for the first time. He was in western dress, his face still hairless, and below his high cheek bones the amber skin, smooth like satin, was suffused with pink. Every feature was exquisitely formed, and the folds which marked his eyes as Chinese were delicate. His feet were so small that he could have worn shoes which Molly had outgrown when she was at school. A westerner, seeing him for the first time, might be excused a desire to stroke him, as a man in miniature. 'No wonder a young English girl like Molly fell for him, and believed him to be the most wonderful of creatures,' whispered Mary. 'Anyone would want him as a pet. Maternal instincts are aroused at sight.' When, however, we got to know him we realized his astuteness as manager of the tannery, and his mature ability in dealing with other people. He spoke not in the local Duliang way, but with a Peking accent; and we sometimes vowed his English had a touch of Yorkshire.

'The meal wont be ready for hours yet,' said Molly as she put down her empty soup bowl. 'Let us ask Mr Yü to show us his pictures.' This delighted him, and he led us into a small room which was his studio. Some of his pictures were mounted on scrolls, a few hung on the walls, but mostly they were rolled and wrapped in cloth squares, the corners carefully knotted together. Some of these Yü undid and held before us. There was a solitary crane, a chrsyanthemum, a cicada on a twig. They were impressions, the emotions of a moment, revealing our language teacher in an entirely new light. He had never spoken to us of his pictures, but now he explained them: the perspective as seen from above, the double shadows, the form, pointing to this or that to illustrate his meaning. He had taken off his glasses and peered short-sightedly at his pictures. On the flat table – for there was no easel – was a work he had completed that very morning. It was a lion, entirely un-British, sitting in benign contemplation. He decided it needed another touch, and moistening his brush on the colour slab he held it firmly, exactly upright to the paper, and added with the delicate point an additional and final hair to its tail.

'Defence not defiance,' commented Wu Deh-min, who had sensed that our western reaction was to regard the lion as ridiculous. He himself had realised at once what the picture meant. Taking advantage of China's weakness the foreign powers had striven to obtain spheres of influence, largely for trade. Japan had strengthened her position in China during the First World War, and afterwards had schemed to increase it further. In 1931 she siezed Mukden, and the following year had established the puppet state of Manchukuo. The indignant Chinese boycotted Japanese goods, and Japan retaliated by fighting at Shanghai and bombarding Nanking. China appealed to the League of Nations. After being condemned Japan withdrew from the League, only a few weeks before we met at Mr Yü's home. Japan had aroused the hatred of China, and given a fatal blow to the League of Nations, thus paving the way for World War Two, although that evening we did not realise the implications of what had happened.

'This lion is our China,' explained Deh-min. 'With a gentle growl or two we are letting Japan know that we are watching. If she continues to attack us, the lion will certainly change and will become aggressive in defence.' The artist nodded in assent, pleased that he had been understood.

'Now we must see his black and white street scenes,' suggested Molly, who was evidently a familiar visitor. Yü, with an apology that they were not real art, but only Chinese-foreign style, needed little encouragement to bring out some small drawings in Chinese ink. They were so delightful that I then and there asked him to do some for me – several appear in this book. Yü was still more apologetic when payment was mentioned, but times indeed were hard. Most people had to undertake several jobs in order to keep alive, and he too was forced to sell his pictures instead of giving them to his friends as he would wish.

The other guests were now beginning to arrive. Wisely

they had waited for the second or third summons. The gateman had changed 'the meal is ready' to 'the meal is coming to the table', and finally announced 'the rice is being eaten'. Then they knew it was time to come, for the food was probably prepared. The usual square table for eight had been covered with a round top, and ten stools were arranged around it.

'Please sit. There is no upper or lower,' Yü Tse-tan invitingly but untruthfully declared as he indicated a stool at the head of the table. The guests politely went through the motions of competing for the humbler seats near the open doorway, but not too earnestly as the host would be embarrassed if his rightful place were not left vacant for him. We ended, as originally intended, with Deh-min and the three western guests sitting in the more honourable places, looking out at the courtyard. Then it was realized that Yü Tai-tai had not appeared.

'It is not our Chinese custom for the women to eat with men. She is busy in the kitchen,' excused her husband.

'But we are here,' Molly and Mary spoke together. 'And it is a new China with new customs,' added Deh-min.

Mrs Yü, a black satin band over her thinning hair, a small lady whose tiny feet were bound, was brought across the courtyard from the kitchen. She was shy and agitated. Another stool was brought, and a place made for her at the foot of the table. She remained only a few minutes, apologizing for the poorness of the fare and inviting us to eat. Then she excused herself to see about the meats and vegetables which, all agreed, were cooked and served in a manner not to be equalled in Wheelbarrow Lane, or indeed in few houses in the city.

Some of the guests we already knew, but this was the first time we had met Bao Hsin-min apart from his official duties. He was head of our branch post office, conveniently placed between the old temple and Hercules Park. When we went to buy stamps he would usually appear behind the counter, rather than trust his somewhat casual assistant to deal with foreign customers. Hsiung Wei-lin we also knew as manager of the sub-office of the Bank of China, situated for safety just inside the main gates of Jen Dah. Both were men of importance in the Lane, Bao married, but Hsiung rather exceptionally still single. Both wore the usual Sun Yat Sen jackets, as was correct for men with official work, but Hsiung was neat and tidy and Bao much stouter and less smart. He soon undid his buttons and, despite the fact that the year was still young, drew out a fan to cool himself.

Most guests noisily enjoyed the food, which was certainly not 'homely' but carefully selected as likely to appeal to western tastes, additional red pepper ground in oil being available for those who might find the food insipid. Yü the host, apologizing for his food, competed with Yü the artist, who explained to us how colour, taste and smell were combined to bring perfection, and how dish followed dish in proper sequence so that taste was augmented and digestion unimpaired.

There was an air of informality, as often happens with even the most formal Chinese occasions, especially if children are about. A cluster of them was outside the open doorway watching the foreigners, commenting on the way they handled chopsticks, and repeating any words they overheard. Every few minutes they were shooed away, but soon returned. Yü's son, who had been seen peeping through the lattice of a side door, was brought in to be introduced to us: a four-year-old, he stood shyly making his bows. He was a small replica of his father, dressed in a long gown for the occasion.

'I am going to cut your head off. Are you afraid?' Bao Hsin-min spoke to him rather sternly. The guests laughed when Yü Go-go rather doubtfully replied: 'Not afraid!'

Then Bao produced a pocket knife, and still more

sternly declared: 'I am going to cut off your finger. Now are you afraid?' This was too much for Go-go. He stood his ground for a moment. Then with tears in his eyes, he ran from the room, followed by shrieks of delight.

Molly, upset by these jocularities, turned to her husband and asked in English: 'Why is it that people always tease children? It is pointless and cruel. They are not playthings.'

'To show power,' suggested Wu Deh-min. But Molly thought it was a strain of cruelty, which had never been deliberately discouraged. She had seen a live rat nailed to a board by small boys who were attempting to pull out its teeth – and this was no solitary incident.

The guests knew sufficient English to understand the general thought, but Wu Deh-min, attempting to cover what might have been considered rudeness on the part of his western wife, made the subject general by saying in Chinese that what upset him was the squealing of the pigs on the way to market as they were trundled over the ruts or uneven paving stones. They were tied on their backs to the wheel-barrows, their bodies torn by tight ropes. It was not all cruelty Bao argued: their long ears were certainly pierced and tied back with string, but it was so that they could see when walking. It was only when they got too tired they were put on barrows. 'And on a hot summer day a man with a bucket of water sprinkles them from a ladle to keep them cool.'

'Or to keep them alive until they reach the slaughter house.' Deh-min was realistic.

Hsiung Wei-lin, more sensitive than Bao, his chopsticks hovering over the crisp-skin fish on its dish in the middle of the table, spoke decisively as a banker should. 'It is recognized that we lack kindness to animals. That is why Gow Chung-ho at his school, Jen Hsiao, keeps rabbits and birds so that the children can learn to look after them properly and be kind.' Then, enlisting the help of Bao Hsin-min, closed the

subject by the two of them using their chopsticks, with a skill born of long practice, to turn over the fish, the upper half of which was already eaten. Yü Tse-tan, with an appreciative 'hao-hao', invited his guests to attack what previously had been the underside.

Molly, however, was still thinking of her own child. She had been making cakes when Han-ku, noticing a peculiarly shaped knife on the table, had asked: "Ma, what is that for?" Then without waiting for an answer had horrified her by saying: 'I know. For killing children!' Her child had said that.

When the token bowls of rice had been washed down with the final soup and the invitation given to sit away from the table, we had taken our cups of tea with us. Molly was still thinking of the responsibility of bringing up her child. She told Mary and myself how a few weeks previously Han-ku had come to her crying. 'They say I am not Chinese, but am a foreign *wa-wa*,' he had told her through his tears. 'I am Chinese. Tell me I'm Chinese,' he had pleaded.

Molly had taken him on her knee and soothed him. 'Of course you are Chinese,' she had assured him, 'but I am your mother and I was not born in China. That makes you look a little different, but you are just the same as the other little boys inside. Daddy is Chinese and you are Chinese too.'

Later some of the children in the courtyard were shouting: '*Yang wa-wa*, foreign baby' and she had heard him say: 'I'm just like you inside. I'm Chinese.' She wondered if what she had said to him was wise. She was conscious all the time that she was treading a path for which she knew no guide. Immediately she corrected the pronoun to 'we' and, in an action entirely un-Chinese, reached out her hand, affectionately touching her husband lightly on the arm.

Cloths, wrung out in steaming hot water, which had been handed round from time to time, were again brought from the kitchen. It was growing dark and Yü Tse-tan suggested that we should see his flowers before all light was gone. At the end of the heavenly well, as a shield to the big end room in which we had eaten, was a wall of evening primroses. He was proud of them, and we admired the bright gleam of the pale yellow flowers, like little lamps in the gathering dusk. He bid us watch the buds in case we should chance to see one opening. It was Hsiung Wei-lin who saw one. He called excitedly as the yellow petals spread apart; and there was laughter and hand-clapping at the joy and beauty of it all. I had not the heart to tell the artist that his flowers were weeds in some places in England; but then we do not have the many lovely moths which already were fluttering amid the bright colours.

As Bao and Hsiung lived near the Jen Dah gates at the places where they worked, we walked together up the Lane as we returned. Bao confided to Mary that he would like to learn more English: it would help him in his postal work and he could read our books. Hsiung, perhaps moved by the talk of children, so much a part of Chinese life, surprisingly told me that he supposed he ought to marry. He wondered if I knew any girl among our students who might be suitable. I was spared the difficulty of other than a frivolous reply, because of shouting in the Lane and people running out of their houses. For a moment we were alarmed; then through a gap between the houses we could see in the distance flames rising to the sky. Within the massive walls, a corner of the city was on fire.

It was a horrifying sight. We knew that section was a crowded one; we realized the terrible distress which must result. Fire-fighting facilities were inadequate. The only effective action was to contain the flames within the high walls specially built throughout the crowded parts of Duliang. Houses in the track of fire were speedily demolished by the fireman, but their owners, like all whose homes were burnt, received no compensation or insurance, except as friends or relatives might help.

We might have noticed the fire sooner, but there were no clouds to reflect the glow. The blaze was too fierce for there to be much smoke: that came later from the smouldering ruins.

Hsiung took a breath so deep that I could hear it above the clamour. 'I always feared this would happen,' he spoke with emotion, his voice almost falsetto. 'It is a place of wickedness. The prostitutes live there, and other evil people. *Tien* – heaven – could stand it no longer. It was inevitable.'

'You think God sent the fire?' I asked.

'Not God – a person.' Hsiung sounded as though it was all quite clear to him. 'It had to happen this way – cause and effect. *Tien* is everything: the world, the universe, the interplay of natural forces.' For him the problem whether *Tien* was personal God or Impersonal Nature, which for generations had worried western theologians, did not exist. 'Wrong relationships, betrayed tradition, must lead to disaster. Peace and harmony can come only from right behaviour. If only men were princely, as Confucius pictured, then everyone under heaven would be happy and at peace.'

We had been more used to students, who were concerned with building a new China, and were more interested in machines for factories, trucks for the new roads, and planes for transport, than in the ancient Chinese culture. Our bank manager was revealed as a philosopher, walking along old paths. Gone was our too superficial evaluation of him as little more than a polite official looking down at us through the metal grill on his high counter. 'Sometimes I believe benevolence and righteousness are dying,' he told us, naming the basic principles. He was quieter now. He was turned towards the fire, and in the darkness there was reflected on his face a faint red glow. 'I fear that within this generation virtue will be lost in China.'

III

Molly and Deh-min

OUR FRIENDSHIP WITH MOLLY and Deh-min developed rapidly. They gave us the opportunity of escape from our self-sufficient university community of staff and students, which tended to be a small semi-western island in a Chinese world. Sometimes we went to their home, but usually they came to ours, as they enjoyed the relative peace of the Jen Dah campus. Fu Lu-chin also tempted Molly, and possibly Deh-min, by making parkin from oats, which he himself ground, together with ginger and the rawest of black local sugar, and by baking oven bread which would not have disgraced a Brightmoor housewife. No trouble was too great when he knew they were coming, for he remained conscious of a debt, difficult to redeem by Chinese standards, because Molly had helped him to get his job with us.

Gradually we came to know the story of their lives. The scraps of information which we gathered from them fitted like jig-saw pieces into a coherent picture. Molly, the true raconteur, possessed the gift not only of being able to recall small incidents, but of making them vivid with remembered conversations.

At first we presumed that Molly's father, a doctor in Brightmoor, had died; later we learned that he vanished with another woman. Emily Spark was left alone to bring up her small daughter. She remained in her large house and made ends meet by taking overseas students from the Technical

College. Before long it was recognized that Chinese students were particularly happy with her, and for as long as Molly could remember they had one or more living with them. The College – those who spoke of it as the Tech were frowned upon – had won fame, particularly abroad, by the quality of its work on leather. It was because his family hoped that eventually he would manage a tannery in the new industrial China that Wu Deh-min was sent to Brightmoor. Following the advice of other Chinese, he sought lodgings with Mrs Spark.

Molly, her schooling ended, much to the envy of her friends, achieved the local distinction of becoming the secretary of Dr Vale, the College Principal. At eighteen she held out both hands to welcome what life had to offer, and, in reaction to the drabness of her life, yearned after beauty. Flowers, their colours, shapes and perfumes, moved her strangely. There were dales and moorland not far away, but Brightmoor itself was not the place for natural beauty. Their home – the old surgery – was in Lilac Mount, but this was a misnomer, like Brightmoor itself. No lilac trees grew there, and over the town there was usually in those days a pall of smoke. The odour from the tanneries was not unpleasing to many who lived there: it symbolized livelihood and the small town's fame – in fact it was scarcely noticed except on sultry evenings when the air was still and heavy.

It had been Wu Deh-min's love of flowers and nature, and the never-never land of wonder and romance from which he came, which called forth Molly's first response to him. Her name, she discovered, conjured up for him the Chinese *mo-li*, the fragrant jasmine; and in consequence he always called her Mo-li, creating for her the picture of a Chinese garden with tender trees and shrubs, bright with flowers of many colours, filling the air with their delicate scent. As their intimacy grew, and their friendship ripened to thoughts of marriage, he told her how he longed to plant his English jasmine in his Chinese garden, tending her with love and affection.

'My dear, you were irresistible,' said Molly turning towards Deh-min who was with us when we were hearing how first they met. 'What chance had a young girl like me? You simply carried me off, and did transplant me.' And Deh-min looked as nearly sheepish as any Chinese I have ever seen, but only said: 'I didn't really say that,' and 'you can't possibly remember.' Indeed I was beginning to feel a little apprehensive, because the one thing one does not do in China is to ridicule others and expect to keep their friendship. The big stick with which children are disciplined is the threat: 'people will laugh'. In self-protection many remarks are prefaced with the well-worn phrase: 'don't laugh at me'. Molly, however, was not poking fun: it had been, and perhaps still was, a poetic romantic spell that bound her to him, though tempered from the first by her clear head.

To marry across national barriers, when so much remained unknown, was not to be lightly undertaken, especially as it meant that Molly, the only child, must leave her mother. 'But Deh-min was always quite uncanny in getting his own way.' Molly explained how the obstacles seemed to fade away. 'Although you might have no intention of doing what he asked, yet he was so pleasant and so plausible that you ended by doing everything he wanted.' He even won over Mrs Spark by telling her how much she reminded him of his own mother in Shanghai.

Molly's mother refused to stand in the way, although before giving her consent she insisted on knowing that his family agreed and were happy that the marriage should take place. One day a long letter in Chinese arrived, and with it a shorter one in English from Deh-min's eldest brother, Deh-fu. The letters had satisfied Mrs Spark, and strengthened Molly's determination that in marrying Deh-min she would adapt herself to Chinese ways. Deh-fu had written: 'If the girl is gentle in spirit and strong in body I would not forbid this marriage. If she wants her own way and wills not to do as we do, she would be unhappy, so do not bring her.'

'So I resolved,' Molly told us, 'to become as much Chinese as possible with my big nose and pink skin.' Deh-min, of course, put it a flowery way. With unconvincing caution he had warned her: 'When you transplant a flowering shrub sometimes it withers, the soil does not suit or the air is wrong. It may be too hot or cold, and there may be people who, thinking it is a weed, will root it out.'

'He told me,' said Molly, 'that it was a great responsibility for him to take me to his China; but I protested that he must not say "his China" any more, for it was mine too. It is ours.' She spread both arms as though to show that she was part of the world around us. 'And that was that,' she concluded gaily.

When Deh-min completed his course and Molly was twenty-one they were married in Brightmoor Parish Church. The Principal of the College, Dr Vale, having first assured himself that she really knew what she was doing, acted like a father and had given her away at the altar.

★

Although Molly's experiences on the ship had taught her some of the social implications of her marriage, it was not until they reached Hong Kong that Deh-min also became personally aware that an adverse reaction to a marriage like theirs was not confined to westerners. One evening, in high spirits, he took Molly to a restaurant famous for its Cantonese cooking. They were at a small table, happily absorbed in each other, when a Chinese of obvious standing came to the door of a private room where he and his friends had just finished a meal. He had drawn back the curtain and was surveying the scene. Then, in a loud voice, he called to those in the room behind him: 'Some of these students who go abroad get thoroughly denationalized. They bring back foreign wives as well as foreign ideas.' A burst of laughter greeted his words. Deh-min flushed angrily, for he knew that he was meant to hear what was said. Molly soothed him and restored his esteem; but after that Deh-min was shy and never went to that place again.

They had started together as two people in love, but it was becoming all too clear that their marriage was reaching beyond themselves. It was an experiment which Molly was determined should succeed. For the sake of their sanity, and their life together, she saw that they must ignore the wounds, and allow victory to their sense of humour.

It was in Hong Kong that they encountered the first real crisis of their married life. 'Molly thought I had betrayed her.' Deh-min interrupted so suddenly that we suspected he was endeavouring to justify himself before the tale was told.

'And I had every reason to believe you had,' declared Molly, softening her accusation by the caress she gave him with her eyes. 'On the ship there was an English girl married to a Chinese business man. She kept telling me that she hadn't the faintest idea how many wives the old chap had, but she was sure he had plenty. And the missionaries did keep asking if I was sure you hadn't a wife at home, because most Chinese were married off by their families when young.'

Deh-min protested that it was not as bad as all that. Molly, however, insisted that it was bad enough. He had never told his parents about their marriage. His father, an officer in the National Army, was often away from home, so it was his mother, living in Shanghai, who managed the family affairs. Deh-min feared she would oppose his marriage with an English girl, even though as third son he was more expendable. His family could have forced him to return to China by cutting off funds. So he had unburdened himself to Eldest Brother, Deh-fu, who was more likely to be sympathetic, and who had indeed agreed to the marriage, but had decided to await a more opportune moment before telling their parents. Now Wu Lao Tai-tai, Old Lady Wu, must be informed, and much more difficult, forgiveness obtained for what she must feel to be a disloyal and possibly displeasing *fait accompli*.

They were staying with Deh-fu, grey haired and a picture of what Deh-min in another decade might become. His Cantonese wife, Yuk-laan, and Molly liked each other from the time they met. 'And my husband never told me what a charming sister-in-law I had,' she accused. She now discovered that he was proud of Yuk-laan and had hoped the two women would be friends and allies, but was afraid lest they should not like each other and so had never spoken of Yuk-laan. Deh-fu practised law in Hong Kong, and accepted responsibility for his youngest brother and for Molly. Without persuasion he set off as soon as possible for Shanghai to attempt to put things right and apologize for Third Brother's unfilial deception, in which he himself had played a part. Until the family was willing to receive them, Deh-min and Molly were to remain in Hong Kong.

They were anxious yet happy days of waiting with Yuk-laan in her home on the steep hillside. They never tired of looking down on to the great banks and high buildings, the churches and markets, and the shops and streets, from which rose the clatter of trams, the hooting motor horns and the constant hum of voices. Across the water, blue in the bright glare of the sun, they could see the nine dragon hills of Kowloon, arid and red. 'When I realized Eldest Brother was to go to Shanghai alone and we could not go with him,' Molly was speaking very softly, 'and for the first time I understood that the parents did not know, I began to imagine what it all might mean. Then I really did begin to feel a little afraid. Brightmoor and Lilac Mount suddenly became very far away.' It seemed as though she was speaking more to herself than to us. 'I remember we were on the balcony looking out over the harbour, watching the moving ships, steamers and wooden junks, their tattered sails set. It was evening and the last rays of the sun were making long shadows which stalked like giants over the hills. The deep blue of the sky was fading; and then in an instant all the colour went out of the world around us.' We who listened felt the anxiety of this girl, faced with the unknown, her assurance shaken.

'But it did come right in the end.' It was Deh-min who broke the silence. The days had lengthened into weeks before the telegram came from Eldest Brother. It stated simply that the Old Parents were willing and impatient to see Deh-min and his bride. Deh-fu himself would have left Shanghai before they could arrive.

Despite the good news which the telegram brought the short sea journey north was full of apprehension. Deh-min tried to prepare his wife for meeting his family. 'In the old days when Chinese married,' he told her, 'we bowed before the tablets of our ancestors, for marriage was a family affair in which those who were dead were still involved. The bride had to kneel before her husband, and bow her head in kow-tow before his parents, to symbolize that by becoming a wife she was also entering a new family as a filial daughter-in-law.' Yuk-laan previously had described how she had knelt and bowed to Old Mother and to all her husband's family when she had married, but what the already-married Molly should do nobody seemed to be quite sure, except that she should show her deep respect. They were path-makers, belonging to a new generation, faced with new situations. Deh-min was one of the many millions stepping from ancient China into a new way of living, baffling, strange, full of fresh problems for which there were no ready answers, for which custom was no guide – and Molly, with all the traditions of the west about her, was adding to the complications.

Wu Deh-min was not with us when Molly told us of their arrival in Shanghai. There were grey skies and a persistent drizzle which conspired with the brown turbid waters of the rivers to make the day a gloomy one. There was no circle of welcoming relations on the dock to meet them: only one servant to help with their luggage in the noisy struggle of the customs examination. If Molly's mind had not already stopped registering impressions she might have been surprised at the luxury of the car in which they drove along the broad avenues of the French Concession, their horn blasting a way through the rickshaws and slower moving traffic.

They turned in through great iron gates set in a wall of grey stone, driving more slowly between firs and evergreens, lovely despite the dull rain. There were latticed pavilions and a small granite pagoda across the lawns. Deh-min shouted excitedly 'We're here,' as they approached the house itself, and then she knew, unbelievably, that this massive stone mansion with its verandahs and colonnades was their home. Servants surrounded them, all talking at once. One old retainer, delighted to see Youngest Master again, led them across the marble hallway. It was deserted, although Molly, now getting more and more nervous, was sure they were being watched by eyes which were hidden. They could hear suppressed laughter and the quick running of feet. It was almost more than she could bear.

They were taken to a bedroom, and Deh-min explained: 'Old Mother says we are to take off our coats, and then see her at once. At least I am to go now, and she will send for you later' – so Molly was left alone. Deh-min she knew was also nervous, and she could not help her own anxiety increasing. The bedroom was western in style, but with a simplicity which was almost stark: it contained so little of comfort. The walls were bare of pictures, but there was a mirror, and as she looked at her uneasy image she remembered how she had looked in her old home. Memories crowded upon her of all that happened since she had left Brightmoor, yet it was as though that entire time had passed more quickly than the few minutes she waited for Deh-min to return.

At last he was back; and from his face she knew that all would be well. 'I have told her everything,' he assured her, 'and she is not such an old tiger after all. She seems very old, and not frightening like I used to think her. Come, get it over.'

They went across the hall to a small room. Scrolls were hanging on the walls, and against them, round the edges of the floor, were pairs of stiff square blackwood chairs with flowered marble backs and seats, and formal tables between them. In one corner was a large table, round and inlaid with mother-of-pearl. What Molly at once saw was the small elderly woman sitting by its side on the edge of one of the great chairs. She was dressed in black silk coat and trousers, her face wrinkled and very brown. Her short-sighted eyes appeared blurred through the unusually thick lenses of her glasses. To Molly it seemed she had never seen a face so full of character, yet so devoid of all expression. It was completely passive, without the slightest indication of welcome or its lack; yet on seeing her, Molly's fears vanished. She saw her as Deh-min's mother, and without premeditation she ran towards her. Taking her two hands in her own, she knelt down before her.

'We have grieved you, and I am offending you because I do not know your proper ways,' she said, thankful that she was able to speak to her in Mandarin. 'Please forgive, and teach me what I should do.' Then she bent over the tiny hands of her Chinese mother and kissed them.

Old Mother, without speaking, took Molly's face between her two hands and looked into her eyes. 'Girl, you are welcome,' she said at last. 'Now get up. The others will want to meet you.'

Indeed they did. They must have been watching for they

burst into the room and crowded round her. Some had wished to come to the docks, but Old Mother had not allowed it. She had insisted that she should see Molly before any of the others.

Molly learned who her newly found relations were, the place of each and of herself in a household run on unfamiliar lines, and the way of speaking to them which she, as wife of the youngest son, was expected to employ. Molly described to us the many relatives and friends who came and went. Eldest Brother, as we knew, was in Hong Kong, but Second Brother, Deh-liang, and his wife Yuin-shao, lived with Old Mother, together with their adolescent daughter and small son. Younger than Deh-min was his sister, Deh-chin. Old Father, Colonel Wu, was usually at Peiping or Nanking on affairs of business or state.

Then followed a period of adjustment for Molly, and indeed for them all. No one in the family group spoke English as fluently as Eldest Brother and his wife Yuk-laan. Usually they chatted in Shanghai dialect, but they could all speak Mandarin, the National Language, as it had come to be called, in which Molly daily became more proficient. Deh-min had started to teach her, even before they were engaged. Molly soon discovered that all activities revolved around Old Mother, not only in the house, but excursions to shops, theatres and friends. When Old Mother went out she always used the car, otherwise she remained at home. Within her embroidered satin shoes, normal in size for the sake of appearances, were tiny feet that had been bound and broken, so that walking was not easy for her. She liked to sit in a low chair, placed so that not only could she see those who came and went across the hall, she also had a commanding view of the doorway leading to the kitchen quarters. She might be short-sighted, but her eyes had eagle qualities, and she rarely missed any detail of domestic and personal life within the home.

★

It was Deh-min who told us how after a time Molly became dispirited. In the busy household she had not found her niche; she felt that she had not enough to do. 'But why should you do anything?' he asked her. 'No one expects you to work. They know you are English and different.' Molly protested that she did not want to be different; and she was tired of being treated as a guest and wished to be one with them. Deh-min was proud that a plan of his proved helpful.

After breakfast, which the family ate as they arrived, some not even bothering to sit at table, the car was brought round to take the schoolgirl Deh-chin to her lessons. On Saturdays she remained at home, and on one of these mornings, after a leisurely breakfast, as they were eating the remnants of fried twisted pastries, she shyly said to Molly: 'Third Brother says that you can make nice cakes. Will you teach me?' – and, after shopping, they spent the afternoon in the kitchen. 'The cakes were a tremendous success,' was Deh-min's verdict. Molly had won herself a place within the household.

Really it was more like an hotel than a home, with Lady Wu as its expert manager. At least eight members of the family were usually there, but others came from time to time, often unannounced, to stay a day or week as suited them. Then, in addition, there were servants to be fed. When the Colonel arrived there were still more guests to be entertained to lavish meals. The servants were never fully trusted to cook on these occasions, except as helpers to Yuin-shao who, with her daughter, followed the detailed instructions of Old Mother, the final seasonings usually being added by the old lady herself. Molly continued to bake cakes, and her Chinese mother came to accept her as a professional colleague. She willingly answered questions about domestic life; and, as Chinese women will, frequently held her hand as they were speaking. Over the *guo* they used for frying and the stove their mutual respect began to grow. Molly was no longer a guest, a curiosity, a western skeleton in their Chinese cupboard, but someone about whom they could on occasion even boast.

When a feverish expectancy descended on the household it was a sign that Old Father was about to visit: floors were washed, windows cleaned, furniture dusted. He was short, like his third son, but thick set, his hair, some grey among the black, close cropped, revealing the shape of his hard head, making him appear both efficient and aggressive. He was an important man, and knew it, swaggering a little in the smart uniform of the Kuomintang army. He was used to giving orders, and having them obeyed. It was unquestioned that he was master of the house, even Old Mother appeared humble before him, though it was known that she had ways of binding him to her will. He always brought his servants with him, and with them his birds, for they, as Molly discovered, were his real passion. He had larks from Nanking, a singing bulbul from Szechwan, and a blackbird. He fed them himself, mixing the powdered egg yolk with tea or boiled water, changing their seed. His servants, all drawn from the army, but clean, well dressed, carried the cages hither and thither, hung them so as to obtain a small beam of sunshine, moved them lest the wind should chill them. Wu would stand for long periods, thoughtfully picking his teeth, watching his pets, hoping to hear a brief catch of song, happy beyond measure when the notes were prolonged.

At first the Colonel said nothing to Molly, although he had recognized her presence by a brief smile and a wave of hand. He spoke little English, and perhaps feared to use it, lest he should appear ridiculous, which would never have done. He would not believe that she might understand if he spoke to her in Chinese, which may have been true as his words were fired staccato with machine-gun rapidity. One day, however, a request, or perhaps an order, came to her through Deh-min: she was to cook the family a western-style meal.

The result was evidently approved, for she was told to prepare a similar meal for some of his personal guests – only with more courses for most Chinese find it difficult to eat to repletion on western food. So Molly had cooked, as a way not to her husband's heart, but to that of her father-in-law. It was the final test; and she passed with honours. Like the other women of the house she watched through a crack as the eight men ate, with noisy appreciation, enough for twice their number. At the end there came triumph: the guests demanded to see the cook. Old Mother led her in, while the guests, proving their ability to speak English, shouted: 'Good, very good. You cook very nice. Bravo!' The real congratulations were of course, for the Colonel, because he now had his own foreign cook. He acquired great face; and Molly was accepted by him and by all.

★

One afternoon, in the shade of a clump of tall feathery bamboos, Molly was drinking tea with us, when her little son, Han-ku, who had been playing with our small daughter, came crying to his mother for comfort. She had sat him on her knee and kissed him. Mary, amused as she watched him return happily to his play, turned to Molly. 'Is that Chinese or western comfort you have given him? Do Chinese kiss their children?' she asked.

We remembered seeing mothers nuzzling their babies as they nursed them on their doorsteps in Wheelbarrow Lane, but we could not recollect having seen one deliberately kissed. 'Anyway I kiss mine,' Molly had declared, and then confessed: 'Yes, I do miss kisses and caresses which my own mother so freely gave. It is true we hold each other's hands now and then, but at first I thought my in-laws most casual.

Old Mother was kind, but solemn and quite strict: her children all had great respect for her.'

In time Molly realized that there was intense loyalty within the family, and also, with few exceptions, real affection. Like the others she had shown her growing love for Old Mother by little acts of service: seeing her cup was always full of hot tea, that cigarettes and matches were handy, and being ready with tobacco and spills should the old lady prefer her water pipe. At the two meals when they sat around the table she joined in seeing that the dainties, the best piece of ham, the tenderest portions of chicken, a boneless piece of fish, were put within easy reach of her chopsticks.

'I suppose husbands and wives do kiss each other sometimes?' Mary had enquired a little daringly, for in those days there were still matters which were not discussed even with closest friends.

Molly had smiled, and did not answer for a while. Then she herself asked a question: 'Have you not noticed Chinese hands?' We had. So often they were long and delicate, almost fragile, yet able to do the most skilled work, carving exquisite ivory or precious jade. Even the country folk could cut intricate patterns in thinnest paper, which would tear in our clumsy hands. Wrist bones, like those in the long fingers, were small and seemed weak, yet actually possessed great strength and power. That Chinese finger-tips were sensitive we knew, for did not the old traditional doctors claim that they could distinguish six different pulses in their patients' wrists, each pulse being sub-divided into three more subtle parts? Merchants successfully bargained, without words which to their disadvantage might be overheard, by the mere touch of fingers hidden deep in their broad sleeves. With loving hands the groom could play upon his bride as on a stringed *pi-ba,* evoking in response the melodies he willed to hear.

★

We were sitting in the window of Molly's home, waiting for Deh-min to return from the tannery. It was already getting towards evening, the sun's rays, coming across the grey roofs, were touching the tops of the osmanthus trees. We wondered if Molly had time to tell us just how they came to our remote corner of China. She was hesitant, and wondered if she could make us understand that living as part of a Chinese family did something to you. After they had been in Shanghai several months she had begun to worry about her husband and also about herself.

'It was really most queer,' she told us, 'almost as though we were being changed by the way in which we lived. I felt that in many small ways I was ceasing to be "me", and was becoming simply part of the family, almost like a bee in a hive. My capacity for making my own decisions was going; my will power was fading.' She began to realize that Deh-min was no longer the same as he had been in England: then he had always something to live for, to hope for. In Shanghai he appeared to have lost all sense of endeavour – he drifted. 'Perhaps it was merely because I was pregnant,' she tried to excuse her dismay at his apparent loss of ambition, 'but I was determined our baby should be born where individuality mattered.' She had wanted to be part of the Chinese family, but not to be absorbed, drained of herself. She tried to make Deh-min understand, and pressed him to do the work about which, when in England, they so often spoke.

'Old Father says to wait awhile. The political situation is uncertain,' he replied to her. She wondered why they must wait for his father, why he could not do something himself. Deh-min was surprised and hurt. 'Do you actually expect me to find a job for myself without his agreement?' – he was most indignant. When she pressed him further, tears came into his eyes. 'I cannot do anything until I am permitted. You don't understand.' He then explained that the real trouble was the Japanese – they were aggressive in Manchuria, and were threatening China. Colonel Wu and his friends would not risk putting capital into a leather factory in these circumstances, although previously they had planned one in Shanghai and another in Tientsin.

Then she suggested that he should attempt to find some other work meanwhile – just to be doing something, to be active. But he had asked her what was the need. 'We have plenty of money. Father doesn't mind. We are all right here. What do you want?'

What did she want? To get away, to escape, for the sake of all three of them, Deh-min, herself and their child. The words of the Reverend John Harlass, when he had spoken of China as the land of buried hopes and dead ambitions, haunted her. She was resolved that the grey mists should not envelop them. She wanted more than anything, for themselves and for China, that their bright hopes might be restored and if possible fulfilled.

She knew that she could not press Deh-min further, so she decided to seek Old Mother's help. One morning, after breakfast, in the early summer, she took her by the hand and led her across the lawn. Old Mother's short uneasy steps, caused by her tiny feet, made the way seem long to a quiet pavilion with low lattice sides, where Molly knew they would be undisturbed. From each of the four upturned corners of the green-tiled roof a small brass bell was hanging. Old Mother was the first to speak, looking at Molly through her thick glasses. 'Now what have you to say to me, child?'

Molly, still holding the old lady's hand, told her: 'You are wise and experienced. I am ignorant and newly come to your country. I need your advice.' And she tried to tell her trouble, picturing what she believed their marriage might mean, the experiment they were making, how she loved Old Mother but felt she was ceasing to be herself, so absorbed in the family that it was hardly any use marrying Deh-min after all. 'I told her that he was already no longer himself, that he was losing his ambition – and then I realized that in my excitement I was speaking English, of which Old Mother was supposed to understand nothing at all.'

But Old Mother laughed and patted her hand. 'Tell me more slowly. Its about Lao San, Old Three?'

'Yes he must get work. We should be together and our baby should be born in our own home.'

Molly's suggestion must have seemed unnatural to Old Mother. 'It is our custom for the children of sons to be born in the old home,' she told her, 'but you come to us from across the ocean. There are many things about which you think differently from us. Yet you are a good daughter, not silly like some. What do you want me to do?'

Molly pleaded: 'To get work for Deh-min; to ask his father, who has so much influence, to find somewhere for him to go.' A light wind came at that moment, and the four little bells all jingled as though they echoed her request.

Old Mother sat quietly. When she spoke the words came softly and slowly: 'I shall see if I can help, but am uncertain if anything can be done.' When they left the cool pavilion they felt the sun beat down upon them as they crossed the lawn to the house.

Some weeks later a large envelope arrived for Deh-min. 'It is a contract,' he explained as he spread out a decorated paper printed in red. 'It is from the Szechwan Provincial Leather College offering me a job as manager of their model tannery. But it is in the backwoods, at Duliang. What shall I do with it? The contract had better go straight back again as a sign I am not accepting it.'

The sheet had been politely folded so that on drawing it from the envelope the first characters to catch the eye were Deh-min's name. Now he started carefully to refold it, putting it back into its envelope.

Suddenly and decisively, as never before in her life, Molly

asserted herself: 'No, no! You are going to accept the contract whatever it says, wherever the place may be. We are
going at last. It is our chance. When do we leave?'

IV

The Devils Go Out

'THE DEVILS ARE OUT: it's going to rain,' Carpenter Deng's apprentices shouted to each other as we passed along Wheelbarrow Lane one sunny day in mid-September. Our astonishment vanished when we saw, close behind us, two French priests in their black summer cassocks, for we realized that it was they who were being taken as a sign of bad weather. Mrs Deng, a strip of blue cloth wound round her head, was sitting on a low bamboo stool in front of the open shop, holding out one of her babies over the convenient drain. She was an acute observer and must have understood the surprised look on my face, for she called across to Mrs Bao, who was just coming out of the post office: 'If Heaven took notice every time our own devils were out we should never have a fine day,' and she laughed loudly at the thought.

We had long since accepted the fact that we who were unlucky enough to be born outside the Middle Kingdom were regarded as *devils from over the ocean*. Mary's eyes, it was true, were deepest brown, like those of the Chinese themselves, and my hair in those days was black, but even if our western-style clothes had not given us away, we could not have hidden our physical differences. Mary's hair, although auburn, was called red by most of our Chinese friends; and my eyes, green-grey, they classed as blue – colours which confirmed us as akin to the traditional devils. ('Why do you call us devils?' Mary had once asked Mrs Bao in a moment of confidence. This had rather nonplussed her, but after some thought she said quite frankly: 'Well, you foreigners do look rather like them, don't you, with your red hair, blue eyes and white faces?')

We were glad that morning, even if Mrs Deng did think of us as devils, at least she felt we belonged. Whatever she may have called us in private, whenever we went to talk business with her husband, she always politely referred to us as 'outside-country-people', or more simply 'ocean-folk'. The small children in the Lane sometimes called 'tall-nose' when they saw us, but this reference to our bigger noses was not really offensive. What we did dislike was when people we passed on the street buried their noses in their voluminous sleeves, or put handkerchiefs over their faces. 'Do we really smell as badly as all that?' I once asked our artist friend, Yü Tse-tan; and from the way he hedged I knew that we did. That the Chinese, garlic eaters all, should find us smelly hurt our pride. To restore our self-respect we maintained that the cause was neither gland nor food, but the perfumed soap we used so frequently.

Hearing Mrs Deng's shouted remarks, Bao Hsin-min came out of the post office to greet us, ignoring his wife who, in best coat and trousers, was going to the city in a sedan chair with one of her small children. 'Where are you going so early?' he asked.

Without hestitation we answered: 'To see Wu Tai-tai.'

'What are you going to do there?'

'We are all going to the tannery.' Would we foreigners never learn? We blurt everything out, lacking all subtlety; and yet our very openness is often mistaken for the greatest subtlety of all. Even the youngest articulate Chinese child would have replied to the first question with a non-committal 'down the Lane'; and as for what he was going to do there he would have enigmatically stated 'business', or (as less likely to prompt further probes), simply 'play' or 'waste time'.

Mrs Bao was now all interest at our revelation. The back chairman was already tilting the poles, but she did not attempt to step over them and sit down. 'How are you going to the tannery?' she asked us.

The roads outside the city were bad. Within the walls they were already widening some of the streets. There were even one or two rickshaws, but they were still so new that they did not venture through the city gates, lest the ruts should damage the locally made springs or the costly imported wheels. Those who could not walk usually used sedan chairs, simple ones like that into which Mrs Bao was about to step, or private ones which could be very lavish indeed. A few people had bicycles; Wu Deh-min went to work on his. The poorer people had to be content with wheelbarrows which jolted when a stone got in the way, or when the wheel had to be jerked out of the well-worn grooves in the paving stones. We were walking to the tannery.

'How can you?' Mrs Bao's anxiety was tempered by having her suspicions confirmed. 'Her belly's not empty' – the usual expression sounding sweeter in Chinese than in English.

Mary assured her that the day was beautiful, we had plenty of time, and Molly was strong and well. Mrs Bao shook her head. Foreigners really were incomprehensible, even the one who was married to a Chinese. There was nothing more to be said to us, though plenty to tell her neighbours. With mutual apologies for avoiding further delay, Mrs Bao and her child settled themselves in the chair. The two men hoisted it to their shoulders and were gone. We followed more slowly, Bao Hsin-min standing outside his office to watch us go.

The barking of the dogs as we approached brought Molly to the door. Although we were anxious to start on this visit which Deh-min had planned for us, there were more delays. The two shopkeepers at the end of her alley wanted to know

from Molly where she was going. Time has no importance on Wheelbarrow Lane. It would be rudeness for us to hurry away too quickly as though we were proud officials or arrogant soldiers. The wine merchant standing beneath the swinging sign announcing 'Tiger Bone Wine', looked at Molly and, spreading his hands expressively over his abdomen, recommended her to buy some of his tonic wine, guaranteed to ensure robust health, indeed to give ferocious courage. From a wide-mouthed earthenware vessel, standing on the green painted counter, he filled a small bamboo ladle and poured it back again, showing Molly the faintly yellow liquid. Along the counter were bottles of the wine for those who did not bring their own containers.

Tailor Su insisted that we step inside his shop. Behind the counter was a long table at which little boys were sewing gowns of silk and cotton. They were far too young, we thought, to be engaged in work needing such skill and concentration, straining eyes over tiny stitches. There was a new pattern, a cluster of peonies in bright magenta, which Su wished to show us. While we were admiring it, the little boys stopped all work and clustered round Molly, who chaffed them into happy laughter.

'The innkeeper: don't look,' she suddenly called to us in English, and making hasty apologies, beckoned to us to follow her, squeezing past the dressmaker's dummy of abnormal proportions, recently coated with aluminium paint, and so out to the Lane. By not waiting to acknowledge him, we at least avoided giving him offence. 'The innkeeper is one of the few people of whom I am not fond,' Molly confessed, 'and besides, if he had started talking we should never have got away,' As we walked she told us about him. He was a reminder of the most unpleasant part of her long journey from Shanghai.

She and Deh-min had both enjoyed the first two weeks, travelling westward on the Yangtse, first by large steamer to Hankow, then on a last surviving stern-wheeler over the shallows to Ichang, and finally on a powerful ship, specially built to force its way to Chungking, mounting the turbulent rapids among the gorges – all so overwhelmingly magnificent. Then followed a week of travel by sedan chair. Molly still cringed as she pictured the bamboo poles resting on the naked, scarred shoulders of the underfed, ragged carriers who bore them and their goods. Some days the men could hardly travel, except after regular visits to opium dens along the way. The last two days of the journey had again been enjoyable: by small junk down the Short River, landing eventually not far from Wheelbarrow Lane, at the *ma-teo,* or dock, outside the South Gate of Duliang, which was indeed the backwoods, as Deh-min had said, very different from the westernized Shanghai they had left so long before. In many ways it was an unknown land into which they had come, so that Deh-min as well as Molly felt inevitable qualms. It was already dark when they arrived; and the boatmen had directed them to the Inn of Peace and Quiet.

Molly continued speaking in English as we threaded our

way through the crowd of blue-clad people on the street. When we were separated she raised her voice, but did not interrupt her story. At the end of Wheelbarrow Lane we crossed the main road, and then over the stone bridge under which the river from the *ma-teo* flowed. There were fewer people on the paths outside the city walls as we went towards the West Gate.

Molly and Deh-min had experienced inns during their journey overland, places with straw-covered wooden beds, on which they spread their oil sheets and their bedding, but no inn had been quite as bad as this one in the Lane. The innkeeper, bowing and obsequious, had ushered them into the upper Official's Room; but that differed from the inferior accommodation only in being less used, the bugs hungrier, the lice more eager, and the dust thicker, so dry that it rose in clouds as they moved. The two nights they spent there were not to be forgotten. It was not clear which was more unhappy: Deh-min who was totally unused to dirt and vermin, or Molly, as always determined to take what came, vainly endeavouring to keep cheerful.

Yet they owed the innkeeper much, for it was he who brought along his neighbour Lee, from whom they rented their present home. There was no suspicion that care for their welfare had been Innkeeper Liu's motive. They never knew what commission he obtained from their landlord, but they were filled with happiness that they had a home of their own, enabling them to live their own lives in their own way, a microscopic cell among China's hundreds of millions, where their uniting love could express the hope which Molly still held of the coming together of East and West.

'Whenever I see Innkeeper Liu I try to forget the bad things,' – the tender Molly was still a little apologetic because we had run away from him – 'and remember that but for him we might have been living in the tannery, in part of a dormitory, sharing the lack of facilities with all and sundry.'

In our walk we soon reached a place where houses and shops ended; there were fewer people and hardly any inquisitive children to press around us. On our right was the grey wall of the city, with untidy huts and hovels clustered at its foot, but to our left were small fields. The rice had recently been gathered in: the cut stalks gave the land a golden colour which gleamed hot in the bright sunshine. Here and there, in the open country, were large farms, surrounded by white plastered walls, topped with patterned tiles, so pleasing to the eye, but so insecure that they were superior to broken glass for discouraging intruders. Above the walls green bamboo plumes waved, and the grey tiled roofs of the low buildings could be seen. A small stream flowed leisurely by the side of the path: from it water was led by a complex network of narrow channels to irrigate the myriad fields.

Molly was the first to see the curving roof of the temple near the tannery. It was still far ahead, and was soon hidden again by the bamboos and the willows growing along the banks of the stream. In its way the tannery had been as much a shock to Deh-min as the Szechwan inns had been. The Leather College had been established in 1924, a dozen years after the old Manchu Empire, which had lasted since the seventeenth century, had been swept away. China's stability rapidly declined after the middle of the nineteenth century, when great national upheavals took place, such as the Taiping Rebellion and the Boxer Rising. Foreign powers had forced their way into the country, establishing rights through 'unequal treaties'. The proud Chinese smarted under these humiliations, but traders, missionaries, as well as Chinese studying abroad, brought new revolutionary ideas – Christian and Socialist, scientific and humanist – which increased the ferment and led in 1912 to the establishment of the Republic, with the leader, Dr Sun Yat Sen, as its temporary first president. The revolution remained incomplete and did not solve China's problems, any more than the Leather

College, founded in response to the urge for modernization, had made any real contribution towards the desired industrialization of western China.

The College had, however, continued to provide positions and salaries for its staff. The Principal, Yang Kwei-chuan, had been a student in Japan when young men flocked there, hoping to learn for China the secrets which would enable her to face the aggressive western world. It was there he met Colonel Wu, then also a young student – a contact which made Deh-min's appointment possible. But for the claims of friendship, there would have been unwillingness for the annual income of the college to be further divided by a new addition to the staff: everything was quite pleasantly drifting along towards inevitable decay on a fixed financial grant from the provincial government.

Amazingly, the first shock over, there was renewed in Deh-min something of the enthusiasm and hope of the Brightmoor days. This was undoubtedly due to Molly, who realized with thankfulness that after all they had escaped from Shanghai before it was too late. With his technical skill, acquired in England, his natural patience, and the tact which so many Chinese possess, Deh-min brought life into the model tannery, attached to the college, securing the acquiescence of his colleagues, if not always their active support. When the news spread that a new teacher, trained in foreign lands, had arrived, many students clamoured for admittance; and Deh-min had chosen two bright young men to help him in his practical work. Now, after three years, he was rewarded by a growing number of students, and the production of a small but increasing amount of good leather.

Faint cries, which became loud and heartbreaking as we approached, made Molly's talk about her husband quite irrelevant. We felt an almost terrifying sense of elemental tragedy. The wailing, so disconcerting, was interspersed with sobbing which sounded inconsolable. It was one of those scenes, so perplexing to the westerner, which makes him realize how little of the lives of the people he really shares and understands. A young woman was sitting by the side of the path, crying, shouting, rocking herself back and forth in her emotion. She was wearing a white jacket and blue trousers like any country girl, but her face was covered by her hands. It was so pitiful, we stood still, anxious to discover if there was anything we could do. A boy and his mother stood before the girl, hand in hand, arguing, shouting, cursing, trying to persuade, now stamping their feet, now each holding out a hand, threatening, entreating.

Molly spoke a few words, but they were not heeded, probably not even heard. Some neighbours, bunched together, were gathered a little way off. One told us: the girl was just married, and the boy her husband. Something had happened – perhaps the mother-in-law, perhaps the boy. She fled and they after her. She would never return home, except to die. They knew she would die. It was the way these affairs so often ended. Perhaps a mouthful of sticky opium, or simply that strange Chinese ability to *ngo chi,* to be so full of hopeless depression, that life sinks and death comes quickly.

'We can do nothing,' said Molly, 'it's no use staying. The misery of China's women – caught in the net of custom. What escape is there for the unwilling captive?' We did not speak. Our feet seemed heavy now, the road hard and dusty: our joy was quenched. In farm and village, grim tragedy was hidden. We foreigners had glimpsed for a moment the unknown suffering, and felt fear, cold and menacing. Molly broke the silence: 'Misery, unmitigated misery.' She repeated the words as we trudged along.

Yet the sun still shone. A child with a string of brown goats cheerfully asked where we were going, and whether we had eaten. Then Deh-min on his bicycle met us, and the child, joined by two others who appeared from nowhere, broke into a sing-song chant: 'Foreign horse, foreign horse, that eats no straw and yet so quickly gallops on.' When we left them we were near the low buildings of the College, by the side of the old decaying temple.

Principal Yang was a delight to behold. He was of the scholar-gentry, old China at its courteous best. He looked both cool and fresh in a grey silk gown, and carried a fan more from habit than for use. One could not imagine that he would ever wear western clothes. On his feet he now had black cloth shoes, his silk trousers bound at his ankles – 'to make it hard for the fleas to go up', Deh-min declared later, ridiculing his principal's old-fashioned ways. Yang, when we approached, opened and closed his fan with a snap, bowed and welcomed us in English, which was clear, if sometimes quaint. For Molly he had a special greeting: 'Wu Tai-tai, has your sweet little baby come down yet?'

From a glance at Molly it was very obvious that it had not; but his politeness called for no reply. Soon we were drinking tea in the college guest room and resting after our walk.

As we chatted it was impossible not to realize that Principal Yang had a paternal fondness for Deh-min and Molly. 'Young people today are sweethearts. They know each other,' he told us. 'The sadness with us older Chinese is that we husbands and wives do not know how to treat each other. The inner person, my home,' meaning, with polite disparagement, his wife, 'and I never knew each other before we married. In some ways this may be better; but in others it is bad. Now in these modern times we should no longer act like our ancestors, but we don't know what to do.' Then spreading out his arms expressively towards Molly and her husband he turned to Mary and myself. 'We are learning from these two. We watch, and learn how to live and work together.'

'Unworthy, quite unworthy,' laughed Deh-min from his chair. Molly declared that she feared the Yangs could learn nothing from her – a westerner, ignorant and young. On the other hand, she could be greatly instructed by Principal Yang in Chinese affairs and by Mrs Yang on how to run a house, as her fame as a housewife was well known. I noticed Molly glance at Deh-min who gave a smile of amused approval at her proficiency in the art of saying the right thing.

When they were rested, Yang Kwei-chuan took Molly and Mary to his home, while Deh-min showed me his work. The classrooms were sensible, though bare, but it was the pits and small factory which interested me. When Deh-min first arrived there were a few skins stretched on bamboo frames, sun-dried and liable to putrify when wet; but now he was making real leather. He used the slow process with vegetable tannins, which grew in such profusion in the valleys to the west; but also he was making chrome leather with imported materials. In Duliang there were Muslims living, so that he was able to secure raw cow hides, as well as the common goat skins. He would have liked more pig skins. It was a matter of sorrow to him that they made such delectable food – hot or cold, seasoned with herbs, reddened with pepper, darkened with soy, sweetened or soured, crisp or so soft that the lumps seemed to melt in the rice.

His leather was increasingly desired by the army for shoes and high riding boots, belts and holsters, saddles for ponies. He could no longer meet the demand. The officers he supplied were deemed lucky. For the men themselves no leather was needed. They wore straw sandals, and, except for the selected few, their uniforms were mostly old, often mere rags held together by string. These soldiers were the curse of China. Originally they were gathered around clever rascals and bandits who, if they gained power, became the warlords who divided up China in the break-down after the Republic was founded. In most parts, but not in Szechwan, these personal armies came under central control when, in 1927, Chiang Kai-shek established the National Government.

As student numbers increased the small hostels were insufficient, so some young men were now sleeping in the temple. Here also old machinery was dumped, for Deh-min on arrival had found much that was broken. The gods from behind their glass windows in the Temple of Ten Thousand Years looked down with bland indifference on these discarded new gods of the modern technical world, piled up at their feet, as useless and ineffective as they themselves. Incense was constantly kept burning before the gilded immortals, but in one hall a new perfume was tickling their nostrils: the fumes from an internal combustion engine which had been placed there for greater security. The electricity it generated was chiefly for some leather finishing machines which Deh-min had salvaged, but also for lighting in which the temple shared. While students worked or idled, worshippers came and went unheeded. They were mostly old women, with tiny bound feet, coming to bow before the gods, seeking protection or cures, while the priest, indifferent to the new world of science, struck the great gong, so that its reverberations echoed throughout the classrooms, ensuring that the Great One, aroused from his doze, was made aware that he was being worshipped and should, in decency, respond.

Yang Kwei-chuan lived in the innermost courtyard of the temple, in a small room along one side of a garden in which ancient cedars grew. Deh-min and I were glad when we joined the others there. Mrs Yang herself brought tea and coloured rice-flour confections, and then returned to her chair, on the edge of which she sat upright, not believing that anything her learned husband and his guests were saying might be intended for her untutored ears. She was a survivor from a generation that has almost gone: she existed to serve her husband, whose property she was. Joy and duty had long since merged into habit, yet she smiled at him from time to time with indulgent pride. Yang himself could hardly have felt any real sympathy with the younger generation. If, as he said, he bridged the old and the new, then one foot was planted much more firmly in the past. He seemed most fittingly to belong to this inner court of the old temple in which, it was rumoured, the priests of days past kept their secret families hidden from the world.

From where we sat we could see the maze of massive roofs, supported by their heavy ridge-poles, with dragons and beasts crawling along them, and down towards the upturned corners. The tips of tall *lan mu,* and Chinese banyans peeped up from the string of courtyards, the varied shades of green vivid against the dusty greyness of the tiles. From the nearest yard there were splashes of dull magenta flowers, half-hidden in the spreading blue-green of crepe-myrtle, so high after centuries of growth.

As the Principal spoke he expressively moved his hands, pointing with his long fingers; but I was not listening to his words. He seemed no longer head of a technical school, using modern scientific methods: he had melted into the past and was part of old China. It was easy to believe that the wisdom of the sages was reflected in his face. He had risen and was standing, like an old Taoist priest, among the cedars, whose branches were gnarled and leafless, their broad trunks misshapen, silvered with lichens, spotted with age. I caught some words: he was speaking of this Temple of Ten Thousand Years. 'The gods are all men become gods. In this way they give hope to all men, that they in turn may also become gods.' For centuries scholars must have strolled beneath the trees, philosophizing, fanning themselves, sipping tea; what a delight he was. No wonder Deh-min had found the tannery in a mess.

When it was time for us to leave, Principal Yang insisted that Molly should use his sedan chair. As demanded by his position, it was one such as officials use: the covered cane chair mounted on graceful poles of curved wood. There were four bearers, two carrying and two running beside them, ready, without stopping, to lift the poles to their own shoulders, allowing those who had been bearing the weight to wipe the sweat from their brows and rest by running empty handed, until once more it was their turn to carry.

'It is good. She will sleep a little,' the fatherly Principal said to Mary and me as we stood at the bottom of the temple steps, watching Molly, accompanied by Deh-min on his bicycle, vanish along the road. 'The motion is soothing and very soon lulls you.' Then, with sparkling eyes, he remembered a childhood scene to amuse us. 'We boys used to sit by the roadside to watch the officials as they were carried swiftly along in their chairs. They were very important men. Usually they hid their faces behind their fans, and their eyes were shut either in sleep or in fear lest recognizing someone they would have to stop and speak. As the chairs passed we boys would give wild cries, and then run quickly off, for had we been caught they would have put a cangue round our necks or had us whipped; but we waited just long enough to see the mandarins start up with fear that thieves were hot upon them.' He was still chuckling as we said our thanks and repeated the conventional goodbyes.

★

Two or three weeks later Molly's baby 'came down', safely and easily. Han-ku led us by the hand to see his little brother lying in a crib of woven bamboo close by his mother. Han-lee's tiny head was covered with black hair, his brown eyes were truly Chinese, and his small nose very flat. Molly, as she looked at him, only knew that she loved him. He was smaller than Han-ku had been; but Han-ku's hair, she told us, had been softer and lighter in shade. 'Of course their names are all part of the family tradition. All the Wu children of this generation, brothers, sisters, cousins, have Han as part of their names, just as his father's brothers and sisters are all

Deh.' But no one called the children by their formal names. Han-ku, the elder was now promoted to 'Old Eldest' or simply Go-go, while his new brother, the 'Old Little One' was Di-di. As a mere baby he was usually 'wa-wa', which very well described his lusty cry.

Molly, of course, was delighted. 'As the mother of two sons my position is assured,' she told us. 'Da-niang, however, takes some credit because she gave me a male kitten a few weeks ago to make sure that the baby would be another boy.'

Deh-min was delighted too. Prestige came from possessing sons and having grey hairs; but he would not allow Molly to feel too much pride. 'No woman in China has any real position,' he made clear to his western wife, 'as a child she must do what her father tells her; and when she is married must obey her husband. If she has sons, then she must take orders from them when they are of age – so now you have another future master, there in the crib.' To complete this male picture of Chinese women, he added: 'Having sons doesn't make it any less important to be a good daughter-in-law' – and Molly was once more back in a world from which she imagined she had escaped.

Lying there in bed she felt a sudden catch in her breath; the joy in her little family might not be as secure as, for the moment, she had let herself believe. She experienced a slight fear that it was still possible to lose herself in the relentless life of the Wu family, which stretched out in time, both into the past where the powerful ancestors still lurked and into the future, but was also strong enough to reach across China and decide the names of her sons. She had snatched Deh-min out of this timeless, almost impersonal, family life and she had made him her own – but perhaps this was illusion. Then she forgot her own fears as she looked at her children: they would love China and all Deh-min's family more completely than ever she could, for they belonged by birth and not just by adoption.

Di-di was sleeping and Go-go had gone down to play. We were quiet; and Mary was tidying the room. It was cluttered with red eggs which neighbours and friends had presented, while the garden was becoming a farmyard with live hens which visitors had brought, either tucked under their arms or in baskets, to the great joy of Go-go who fed them and chased them until, one by one, they went into the pot or were given as presents to others. In the silence as we watched Mary filling a drawer with the eggs which she had gathered from the tables and chairs, I realized how our friendship with Molly had grown. She had given us a new understanding, had transformed Yü Tse-tan from teacher into friend, had made Hsiung Wei-lin and Bao Hsin-min real persons and given us a cook who was able to open many small windows into other people's lives. Could we hope that we in turn had helped Molly by relaxing a tension she must have frequently felt, although rarely acknowledged. Our backgrounds were sufficiently similar for us to appreciate the significance of thought and word without the long explanations which different cultural standpoints sometimes made necessary. Unconsciously we supported each other and found an inner contentment which was not easily come by in Wheelbarrow Lane.

Then came a distressing period. A fever was sweeping through the homes in the Lane: one of those virus infections which make the Chinese feel indisposed, and the newcomers seriously ill. Molly was one of the sufferers; but when she was better she found to her dismay that she could no longer feed little Di-di. The Chinese in general do not drink cow's milk: they find it hard to digest, describe it as containing 'fire', upsetting their health. The cows, which are used on the farms, are not kept for milking, but, their work days over, are eventually eaten by the Muslim community. Molly had been buying cow's milk for Go-go from the small agricultural unit at Jen Dah, but the season was dry, few cows were in milk, and the supply could not be increased. The street shops stocked no powdered milk, and sweetened condensed milk which they bought was not only expensive, having come from the coast, but Di-di did not thrive on it, slowly losing weight.

It was the first time we had seen Molly in tears. Mrs Yü had come over the way to bring comfort. Like her neighbours, who were adepts at coping with the many crises which so largely made up their lives, she knew from bitter experience that actions not words were required. Unless trouble can be averted or a compromise found, it must be accepted and then forgotten. 'We Chinese always get a wet-nurse in such circumstances,' she was saying. 'You must get one at once.' She told Molly of the tea-shop inside the South Gate of the city where, every morning, women gathered who wished to hire themselves out. 'You must send your *da-niang* tomorrow to hire one: but mind she gets someone healthy.'

Molly revolted at the idea that some other woman should nurse her child; but had to confess that it was sound common sense. This was no time for sentimentality. Deh-min accepted the situation without question. 'Of course Mrs Yü is right,' he said, but agreed that it was a matter for themselves and not for their servant alone. He suggested that he and Da-niang should go to the women's tea-shop; but Molly insisted that she should go too.

When they stepped into the shop it was full of blue-coated women, some sitting at the square tables, other standing in groups. Their faces were mostly unhappy, a few pock-marked, all anxious, many full of greed. They were seeking positions as servants, but a number wished to be hired as wet-nurses. Their own children had died, or their families were large beyond possibilities of support, with no other rice-winners, so that they were compelled to sacrifice their own babies who, while they lived, were fed on the water in which rice had been boiled, or with the left-overs of their own milk.

Molly shrank back, clutching Deh-min's arm. 'We must get someone happy, someone young and happy,' but there seemed no such person. 'Let us go home again,' she implored in a whisper. 'If I rest more perhaps I can manage. Nothing could be worse than this.'

Deh-min felt a little indignant. 'I knew it would upset you. You should have let me come by myself as I wanted. We must get someone for Han-lee.' He himself was so upset by the situation that he used his son's formal name, then more kindly added: 'But of course, we must find someone you like,' and Molly had pressed back her tears.

In a corner, away from the crowd, a young woman was sitting. For years to come, Molly and Deh-min would argue about who saw her first. She was a raw country girl, tall, buxom and strong, a white cloth wound round her head. She rose as Deh-min asked if she wanted to hire herself out.

'We need a milk-mother for our small baby,' he told her.

'I have milk,' she said simply, unbuttoning her gown to show them her breasts, swollen and heavy.

'Where is your own baby?' Molly asked her.

'*Diu-lo*, thrown away.' The girl did not waste words.

'That means it is dead,' Deh-min explained to his wife. 'Country people speak that way of babies who die.'

'Ask her about it. Was it illness?'

To Deh-min's question the girl answered: 'Ten-day sickness,' and Molly knew that it was one of the multitude dying from lack of proper attention at birth.

'How old are you?'

'Seventeen, more or less' – she was not quite sure.

'The poor child,' Molly was now full of pity, 'to have lost her baby like that. Let's take her. She looks as though she needs some kindness.'

Deh-min laughed at the change that had come over his wife, and assured her she need have no great sorrow, for

wet-nurses get very well paid, with clothing provided as well
as good food.

When they offered to take her the girl became doubtful.
She had heard about foreigners, but had never seen one
before. Her eyes were modestly cast down to the table, but
her furtive glances at Molly were filled with fear. Others in
the room had been watching with interest, commenting on
scraps of conversation they overheard. Now an older woman
shouted across to her: 'Don't be afraid. All foreigners are rich.
You should count yourself lucky.' The rest of the women,
anxious as any Chinese crowd to take part in the bargaining,
encouraged her to accept.

At last the matter was settled, on condition that the girl
should be proved healthy, free from the diseases so rampant
in Wheelbarrow Lane, as elsewhere in China. Molly had
thought of the possible dangers to Di-di's health, if not to his
life, and the list seemed unending: T.B. and V.D., parasites,
trachoma, skin diseases most loathsome, quite apart from
infections like typhoid and typhus, and the bites of mad dogs.
She had wondered how in the midst of all these any human
survived; and then understood why so many did not.

From home they sent the girl, under Da-niang's care, with
a note to Dr Langham at the Jen Dah clinic. When she returned, wide-eyed and startled, more frightened than ever, she had
a clean bill of health. 'Take her,' the return note said. 'She is
medically clear, but entirely stupid and uneducated. She will
give your baby all that he needs. She is a healthy animal,
young enough to be trained.'

So Liu milk-mother – Lai-ma – became part of their
growing household. Di-di thrived and grew strong, Molly
became her usual self once again, and Lai-ma was tamed.
She was only a child and, discovering a kindness and security
unknown in her previous life, her first fears soon left her. She
became full of new happiness, attached to the family with a
jealous devotion, enjoying experiences in the big city which

she could not have imagined from the little hut with mud walls and thatched roof, away in the country, about which she told strange tales to Go-go and our daughter Mei-mei.

One day in late autumn, when the sun was shining and the air was warm as an English summer, Molly and Mary decided that we should all go by boat for a picnic – an event which we looked back on with pleasure during dark days ahead. At the back of the garden, behind the Wus' house, there was a small gate – the 'safe gate of escape' – which led to a narrow strip of waste graveland, then across a mud path to the river, which wound eastward up to the *ma-teo*, the wharves where junks exchanged their cargoes, mostly come from the distant coast, for the silks, medicines and other local produce intended for Chungking and beyond. A short distance to the west the river turned southward, passing under the bridge over which we had crossed on the way to the tannery.

A boat which Cook Fu had hired was waiting. It was a small pleasure craft with a pink cotton awning supported on poles to give shade for the low bamboo chairs set round a small table. At the stern a few planks made a platform on which the boatman could stand. The inevitable cluster of people, male and female, young and old, gathered to see us embark. Mostly they stared in silence, but some made loud comments. Deh-min worried them as they could not be sure whether he was Chinese or foreign. He and I were in shorts and informal shirts, glad to be rid of the long trousers, the collars and ties which, in those days, our positions demanded. Opinion was sensitive about women's dress: Molly conformed by wearing a Chinese gown and Mary by a blouse with long sleeves and high neck. The main interest was, of course, in the children – always the means of happy relations with even the most difficult crowd. Our two cooks had prepared food, but they remained on the bank as, together with Lai-ma, we set off down the river.

It was always a joy to escape for a time from the crowded Lane and the routine of the Campus. We drifted with the current, the boatman scarcely using his oars, except as a rudder. Once under the bridge we entered a new world: dried paddy fields on both banks, farms here and there, great bamboo wheels turned by the current, with a continuous melodious creaking, raising the water in small bamboo buckets. There were black buffalo with caliper horns lying submerged in the brown water, their little boy-masters watching them, or asleep on the bank. Farmers paused in their work to look at us, but two men, irrigating their land with a dragon-backbone treadmill, were too engrossed in their gossip to see us pass by. There were greetings to be exchanged with all whom we saw, especially the children who ran by the side of the river keeping pace with our boat. Go-go and Mei-mei had sticks to be sailing as boats; and their parents were anxious lest they tumbled in. The boat-man, smoking a cheroot in his long bamboo pipe, scarcely uttered a word; perhaps he was thinking Cook Fu had struck too hard a bargain. People who had leisure to idle must have money to spare.

It was an ordinary family picnic, and yet has remained a happy memory during the anxious years which followed. It was a landmark, the top of a hill, that autumn of 1933: life afterwards was never again quite the same. The road into the future beyond the hill-top led to unfamiliar country, the scene gradually changing, becoming wilder, where fear lurked in the shadows. The quality of life in China tended to be elemental: beauty and ugliness, goodness and evil, kind-ness and cruelty, each stark, rarely blended or softened. Up to that time in Wheelbarrow Lane, light and darkness, joy and sorrow, more or less balanced each other; but now darkness increased and sorrow was more widespread.

In the brightness of the full autumn moon, and with the warmth of the day still about us, we delayed our return. As we neared the bridge the priests in an old Buddhist temple were already intoning those prayers reserved for the evenings when the moon is new or full. The still air around us rever-berated as, with magnificent abandon, the chanting monks worked on their drums, caressing soft whispers from them, then rising to a terrifying crescendo, accompanied by the clanging of gongs, only to let the sound die away to the gentlest rhythm which, with the men's voices, came softly across the quiet water.

As we approached home we could see in the distance the lights of the *ma-teo*, the raised heavenly lamps shining above the dull glow from the street. The cries of the boatmen as they made all safe for the night were blended to a murmur. Molly and Mary had been singing, but now were silent. Our boatman, standing at the stern, stamped gently with his bare foot as he worked his two oars with an unfaltering slow rhythm, soothing to hear. Go-go was already asleep on his father's knee, and Mei-mei on mine. The water rippled gently against the sides of the boat, the sound rising and falling as we were pushed forward against the slow current. A woman on one bank was belatedly calling her pigs with a shrill 'lu-lu, lu-lu'. On the opposite side the high city walls were mysterious and, in the moonlight, a little forbidding. Beyond the boat's awning, in the prow, Lai-ma was sitting. She was still softly crooning an old Chinese song, such as country folk, throughout hundreds of years, must have sung to their babies. One arm was around the satisfied Di-di who had sunk to her lap and was lying asleep. Her gown was still open, thrown back, her young breasts and face bathed in the soft light. It was all unforgettable – sheer beauty and peace.

V

New Year and After

———◆———

THE WELL-BEING OF ALL who lived in Wheelbarrow Lane was watched over by a stone lion. This great brute, which really looked more like an overgrown Pekingese dog, lived in an arched kennel of brick at one side of the Inn of Peace and Quiet. Beggars, hoping to acquire merit, cast at its feet their gatherings of waste paper on which were venerated words written or printed. There the paper burned, so that both lion and dwelling were coated in thick black tar. That morning the beast, seated on its haunches, looked gay: round its neck a bib of bright red silk had been tied and over the kennel itself red paper was draped. Sticks of incense, newly stuck in the mud, were burning before the curved entrance. A young man, whom I recognized as one of the carpenters employed by Deng, had thrown down an offering of paper, with writing upon it, and while it burned he knelt, repeatedly bowing his head to the ground before the lion. It was the time of New Year.

As I stood watching, Artist Yü joined me, his thin body made stout by his warm padded clothes. After the mutual wishes for wealth which the season demanded, he pointed with his chin towards the lion: 'I hope this young man will get what he wants. We all need protection these bitter days.' His arms were crossed, his hands snug in the opposite sleeves, but it was not the weather to which he referred. 'Perhaps the old lion will be as helpful as anything. Our new leaders do little, except help themselves. Evil prospers.'

Wheelbarrow Lane, I thought, had deteriorated steadily during the eighteen months since our river picnic. Yü Tse-tan did not believe there had been such a sudden change. 'It has been slowly getting worse since before the empire ended. Previously it was hidden, but now everyone feels it. The rising cost of rice affects us all. Then there are the soldiers.'

He had no need to say more: I knew what he meant. Soldiers were everywhere – mostly the private troops of military despots, who struggled with each other for power. Many of these soldiers were little more than children, but they possessed guns which they were liable to use. They took what they wanted: food, lodgings, fuel or women. The people were sullen, helpless, no one dared oppose them. Every morning before dawn we were awakened by discordant blasts from buglers practising on the city walls, and raucous cries *i-er, i-er,* one two, one two, *i-er-san-sze,* one two three four, as soldiers drilled on the few open spaces between the Lane and the river.

'China is modernizing along wrong lines and too quickly,' Yü thought. Certainly there were surprising changes every time we went into the city. Old houses were either pulled down, or the smaller ones pushed back to make way for new roads. The number of rickshaws was increasing rapidly. Also one or two newly arrived cars hooted their way through the crowds. The ancient narrow flagged paths of the countryside were being made into highways – 'horse roads' they called them – linking Duliang to other towns and cities so that a bus could travel in one day a distance which previously had taken a week or more. An air-field outside the North Gate was being completed, and a small post office plane was already flying twice a week to Chengtu, the provincial capital, and to Chungking, where there were links with Shanghai and Hong Kong.

'Our Szechwan province is too cut off from the rest of

China.' Yü Tse-tan never forgot his lasting responsibility to teach me, for once a pupil always a pupil. 'The mountains of Tibet to the west; north and south high mountains too; the only road in and out is by river through the gorges, and they are narrow and dangerous. The way to Heaven is not more difficult than the way to Szechwan,' – and he gave a little laugh of pleasure as he always did when he was able to quote an appropriate proverb or popular saying. As we walked along he told me how in the past, people had come from every other province, bringing their customs with them, until Szechwan became the very essence of China. 'We are separate, apart, our land is fertile, our farmers and merchants rich. When Chiang Kai-shek established his Kuomintang Government in Nanking he could not easily conquer us. Our soldier governors, with their private armies, were too powerful, the roads into the province too difficult, so face was saved all round by our local generals giving lip-service and the Central Government confirming them in their positions.' Yet this association had brought many changes: some schools were modernized, a few hospitals built, the country opened up and opium no longer grown in parts where it could easily be seen. But at heart the province remained separate, and as far as they could the local military leaders still went their old ways.

We were standing near the coffin-maker's shop and Old Dzen himself was hanging out a flag tied to a bamboo stick. All down the Lane, bright for New Year, similar flags were flying among red paper streamers. They were the Kuomintang white sun of equality, rising in its blue sky of liberty on a field of red, symbolozing fraternity, which alone of the three had meaning in the Lane. 'We are very loyal, you see,' there was irony in Yü's voice, 'flying his flags although Old Chiang has forbidden us to celebrate New Year in this way. He says we must forget our old lunar festival and keep January first, like other civilized countries.' He chuckled a little. 'As if we were not civilized long before other people.'

Above our heads a length of white cotton cloth stretched from the tea-shop to a tree at the end of Hercules Park. There were large red characters on it, and under them in black English lettering: Szechwan for the Szechwaneses. Yü was wiping his eyes, which watered in the cool air, and then dextrously blew his nose, first down one nostril, then the other – but not with his handkerchief for that was safely tucked up his wide sleeve. 'Not true for long now,' he commented, 'a big change is coming and coming soon.'

The Lane was a blaze of colour. Apart from the bunting and the banners there were brightly coloured paper gods who glared fiercely and protectively from every door on which they were pasted. Most of the shops had hung out pairs of appropriate sayings written in bold characters on red paper scrolls. There were two at the entrance to Jen Hsiao; but they were written, probably by the headmaster Gow Chung-ho, in a form which I could not understand. Yü Tse-tan, pointing with his long finger, read the words to me, while I tried to discover their relationship with the characters as I had learnt to write them. 'Heaven sees as the people see', was down one side, and 'Heaven hears as the people hear', down the other.

'Is that sound Christian philosophy?' I asked.

Yü was not sure. 'But the words are beautifully written, an example for any child to follow.'

The shops and houses had all been cleaned, both inside and out. The cobwebs which had been undisturbed for a year were dusted away. Even the floors of the Inn of Peace and Quiet had been swept. Brightly coloured toys and sweet-meats were for sale on stalls by the roadside, also masks, bright paper lanterns, shaped like rabbits or fish and, for the boys, wooden pikes and swords like those of ancient China. Folk from the country were thronging down the Lane towards the city. On a wheelbarrow, pushed through the crowd, sat a youngish woman in green silk trousers which reached to her ankles, her pink silk gown turned back over her knees, safe from splashes, for it had rained the previous day, and there were puddles in the mud, softened by so many feet. There were pretty young girls and women in plenty, in their stiff new black trousers and short blue padded jackets. The older women carried fire-baskets, stopping now and then to gossip or rearrange the glowing charcoal, more concerned to keep their cold fingers warm than to appear in fine clothes. Few old men were without bamboo pipes and many were wearing their wind-hoods, protecting both head and shoulders.

All the shops had their shutters closed, leaving only a crack through which to squeeze in and out. A measure of prosperity was the length of time the shop remained shut. A few years back, a fortnight or more was usual, but this year it was feared that few could afford to be idle for more than a day or two – although face might demand that the shop remained closed while business was done through the crack in the shutters. It was a time of family feasting, visiting friends, and for young and old the mild excitement of playing all manner of games for coppers.

Mary and Mei-mei spent most of the day with Molly; and during the afternoon I went to escort them back home. Mei-mei, because she was a fair-haired foreign child, aroused so much interest that she needed protection from those who wanted to touch her. The people were friendly, but frightening for her when they crowded too closely around. When I arrived Go-go was chasing a hen in the garden, watched by Lai-ma who was shouting: 'You! a person who eats rice! Why haven't you any sense?' There was scorn on her face as she watched him attempting to catch the fowl, which was getting more and more flustered.

'Stand still! Do it this way.' Lai-ma could be patient no longer. She called to the hen as if it were to be fed, and skilfully grabbed it, tying its legs together with a piece of straw. Then, holding the surprised fowl by the wings, passed it to Go-go and told him to put it in his basket. Together they went to give it to Mrs Yü as a New Year present.

Molly's servants were all in new clothes. The cook and the boy had dark blue gowns, still stiffened with size and smelling of the indigo vat. Da-niang was also in blue, padded for warmth and entirely shapeless. She trotted about on her small feet, the white half-moon patches rising up from inside her green velvet shoes. Lai-ma, who had remained with the family to look after Di-di, now over two years of age but only six months ago fully weaned, was more resplendent, as befitted a young big-footed woman. With the help of Tailor Su, she had made a new black jacket, padded with waste silk, and striped satin trousers. Her old home was now forgotten, and the mystery of her dead child's father never completely unravelled. As time past she became more convinced that, although she had been married, her husband by now would have another wife. Lai-ma herself was just one of the many who went from the country to the city, not to be heard of again.

Mei-mei and the two boys were chasing each other, all wearing bright papier-mâché masks of the Laughing Buddha, that jolly fat-bellied fellow, no other in fact than the Messiah still to come. The boys had new spinning tops, and Mei-mei a bamboo diabolo, from which Lai-ma alone was able to coax a low singing note.

Molly said little, and seemed distraught. Deh-min was not at home. Go-go and even Di-di were going to a school party at Jen Hsiao, so Mary pressed Molly to return with us, until it was time to bring the boys home: but she would not.

'Is anything wrong?' I asked Mary as we threaded our way up the Lane.

'Yes and no,' she replied vaguely. But when we were back

on the Campus and Mei-mei had run on ahead, she told me that Molly indeed was disturbed. Deh-min had vanished.

It had happened at New Year twice before. Perhaps he was seeking relief from new problems by adopting old ways. In previous years he had gone for a number of nights, playing mah-jong and gambling with colleagues and friends in the city. 'It is our Chinese way at New Year,' he had told her. He returned as suddenly as he left and declared: 'It was a stupid waste of time and money; and the wine leaves only a bitter flavour.' For him life went on as usual, but for Molly a new fear was added, forgotten for most of the year.

She knew he would return unannounced, just as he had gone without saying a word, but she must be at home when he came back. It was not only his family who might take him from her, she felt, but at this season she knew that her hold over him was weaker than the call of China. For most married couples there is much in the world around them to keep them together, but for Deh-min and herself she knew that their environment could be disruptive. Had it not been for her sons, so thoroughly infected by the gay spirit abroad, she would have found New Year an empty sadness. She had remembered for Mary the old Japanese proverb: Children are hinges to keep people together.

Mary had promised that I should go to Jen Hsiao to see that the children went home in good time, as Lai-ma knew nothing of clocks. I found them reluctant to leave the other excited young children, but at last were led away. Go-go held my hand, but Di-di was carried on Lai-ma's back. He was wearing his new animal hat, designed to deceive the devils into believing that he was no human child to be molested, but only a beast. Lai-ma lit up the path with her new paper lantern, although on ordinary nights we were content to use torches of dried bamboo rope. At the sides of the Lane there were small stalls in front of the closed shops, dimly lit by the smoky glow of rape-seed-oil lamps. Oranges

and peanuts in neat little piles, cigarettes in pairs and single cheroots were offered for sale, also purses and knick-knacks and bright metal frames, their tawdriness hidden in the gloom. Outside the full tea-shop, standing in the thin drizzle, people were listening enthralled to the story-teller reciting familiar tales. We stayed a moment to listen as, with eloquent voice and meaningful gestures, he conjured up Chuko Liang from the ancient Three Kingdoms. We then hurried the children back to their mother. Their father had not yet returned.

★

General Chang, the Military Governor of Duliang, was in trouble. A number of years previously he had been able to build up his private army to sufficient strength for him to end his bandit days and come to satisfactory terms with the powerful governor in the provincial capital, Chengtu. Chang was fortunate that the territory he held included some salt wells, which were a great source of revenue. Stomach and bowel complaints had recently spread among the soldiers who guarded them. A score or more had died after convulsions and paralysis, and a large number were ill. The General believed they were poisoned by local people and was preparing revenge, but first asked the Jen Dah medical school if they would investigate.

Dr Williamson, the Dean of Medicine, a tall Canadian, whom the Chinese respected, went to the wells. After autopsies he confirmed poisoning, which was thought might be due to barium salts. He suggested that the Department of Chemistry should attempt to investigate further before Chang started chopping off heads. Su Ten-chi, my colleague who was shortly going to Oxford for post-graduate study, Chen Deh-li, a promising student, and I set off with some simple apparatus to see what we could find.

We soon learnt the cause of the trouble. The brine, slowly drawn up by bamboo ropes from the exceedingly deep wells, a few pints at a time in wide bamboo tubes, contained barium salts, but unlike the brine from other districts no sulphates which would have rendered it harmless. There was a time-honoured custom, the reason for which had long since been forgotten, that when the brine was concentrated in the salt-pans, and salt removed, the last liquor should always be thrown away. Despite local protests, the soldiers insisted that these liquors should be evaporated to dryness, so that they could obtain more of the wealth-giving salt. Unfortunately their cupidity meant that this final lot contained an appreciable amount of barium chloride. Lao Du, the chemistry coolie, who had carried our equipment, felt it was the justice of Heaven that the soldiers should die in consequence of their greed and rejection of local tradition. He agreed to our giving the simple advice which would prevent others being poisoned by the impure salt, but declared 'the sooner the *bin-ber* kill themselves off the better for everyone' – using the popular contemptuous term for the troops.

When our work was completed, we set off before daybreak to be sure of reaching Duliang before dark. We walked briskly in the cold early morning, climbing the narrow flagged path leading out of the valley. Although dawn was breaking, it was too dark to see into the soft mists around us. We could hear the barking of dogs and the sleepy cries and the coughing of men as they roused in the farms. In the distance a cock was crowing; then another, and another. Soon the smell of wood smoke reached us in the damp air. Day had come when we reached the top of the hill and sat down to rest by a small wayside shrine under a lonely tree.

Below us, on both sides of the pass, the valleys were filled with grey clouds, drifting and billowing in the light airs which come with the dawn. They revealed the hilltops and then hid them again. On the high ridges there remained a few trees, which had escaped being cut down for fuel. We were stirred, as in a Chinese painting, not only by what we saw, but by what we imagined. Szechwan has a beauty which is all its own. It is a great bowl, surrounded by mountains, where the air is so still that clouds collect. Even the dogs bark when they see the sun, the proverb tells us; and the neighbouring province of Yunnan rejoices, as its name makes plain, that it is south of the clouds.

'O Mi Teo Fu' – slowly Lao Du read the words which were carved on the pilgrim stone pillar, erected near the tree. This ancient call to the holy Buddha, repeated through the

ages by countless millions of men and women, expressed the
lift of the heart which we all experienced that morning. The
coolie and a friend of his were helping to carry our bedding
rolls – for we never dreamed in those pre-liberation days
that we might carry our own and yet be esteemed. To them
the tree was much more than wood and shade-giving leaves:
it had a sacredness which made it an object of worship, and
had protected it from rapacious wood gatherers. They read
with laborious tedium the votive inscriptions stuck in the
bark by those who were thankful for shelter from the midday
sun or who hoped for journeys speedily accomplished and
safe from robbers.

Up and out of the mist two carriers were climbing,
hurrying along. Each was bearing two oiled waterproof
containers in plaited bamboo frames. They paused for a
moment, taking the weight from their shoulders by suppor-
ting their carrying poles on their resting-sticks. Then one of
them called me by name. This surprised me for I had no idea
who he was.

'It's Lao Lo, the fish-man's son,' his companion answered
for him, when I asked his worthy name. 'You know his
father's shop in Wheelbarrow Lane.'

Indeed I did; and this was the fish-express. The lovers of
delicate fish always believe that those from more distant
rivers tasted better than those from the local streams and rice
fields; so fish were carried alive from places several days
journey away in these special containers, filled with water
which was changed at convenient rivers. Sometimes a relay
of carriers made it possible for the living load to be hurried
along by night as well as by day. When it was possible to rest
a short night on the journey, the containers were left immer-
sed in a nearby stream.

'Sit and rest your breath a little,' we called to the men. But
they would not.

'Unless we hurry some of the eating houses of Duliang

will be short of good fish.' Lao Lo was already lifting his load to his shoulder.

'And the Lo family will be short of money.' His companion laughed, for it was common knowledge that they were the wealthiest, and one of the meanest, families in the Lane. Away the two men went with a graceful swing of their loads, their skilful quick movements so timed that not a drop of water was spilled.

'You did not realize that Wheelbarrow Lane stretched a day's journey into the country,' Su Ten-chi teased me, for I must often have amused, if not bored, my Chinese colleagues by talking about my friends.

A few days later, when I was returning along the Lane from the city, I saw Cook Fu buying fish. His basket was over his arm, but with the other hand he was twisting the hair from his nose. He was obviously agitated. When he saw me he called: 'Hsien-sen, please come.'

Lo, the fish-monger, a thick-set man with sparse moustache, was standing gloomily behind his bowls and tanks in which fish were heaving, too plentiful to have space for swimming. They were always sold alive. Fu had just bought one, and as he talked he moved his other purchases on top of it to keep it from flapping. 'It's *la-fu*, the pressgang,' he explained, my heart sinking. I knew that recently soldiers had been on the move, commandeering any man they could find to carry their equipment. I had seen a group of their captives, roped together, led up the Lane and locked in the tea-shop until sufficient men had been collected. One man I noticed was middle-aged, crying bitterly, beseeching the soldiers to spare him: he was too old to carry, he was ill, he must work for his mother, she would die, and his wife and his children, they must eat. The soldiers were deaf to his entreaty. As the man struggled they merely pulled the ropes tighter.

'His son has been taken,' Cook Fu was saying.

'Not the one who carries fish from the distant rivers?' I pictured again that early morning encounter.

'Just that one,' broke in the fish-man. 'The two of them came with their loads of fish and set them down there in front of the shop' – and he pointed to one of the containers – 'then came the soldiers' whom he cursed amply and loudly and also their mothers who had misbegotten them. 'The soldiers came suddenly, and jumped on them before they were aware. The other was too quick. He got out his knife, cut the ropes and ran. The soldiers threw stones at him, but he got away. How everyone laughed! But they got my boy.'

'They took him away, tied him with ropes. The bastards! Sons of tortoises, all of them.' It was a woman's voice. Hearing us talk she had come out of the inner room. She was Lo's wife, and was followed by her daughter-in-law. The fish-monger did not take kindly to this interruption. It was men's business, not for women to open their mouths. Brusquely he ordered them back. The older woman, determined to say her word, called as they retreated: 'We don't know if he will ever come back. Often they don't. You never know' – and there was wailing from the inner room.

You never know – the lack of security was the only certainty in which the Lane people shared. The men who were taken away were given food, but usually no money. If they were forced to carry for many days it was often difficult for them to get home again. Sometimes in desperation they themselves became soldiers. Lao Lo had already been absent four days, but he was strong and used to carrying. Fu Lu-chin spoke up for the fish-man. 'We have been thinking,' he was speaking in his most persuasive manner, 'that perhaps you might be willing to help. See the Military Governor, General Chang, perhaps? He will get Lao Lo sent back for you.'

The prestige of the foreigner still lingered in China, despite increasing outbursts of anti-foreign feeling. When our servants were caught by the pressgang they would claim that unless released foreign troops would be sent. Unlike the articulate students, the ordinary people were not yet disillusioned and believed we westerners, who were still in China under extra-territorial rights, had power. I was noncommittal in my reply, knowing I could do nothing.

'They are frightened of foreigners. They will do something if you order them.' It was the women back again. Lo raised his fish knife in a threatening gesture, but dropped it helplessly when he saw they were crying. He echoed their hope that as a powerful foreigner I would help them.

Happily, next morning Lao Lo returned. He was fortunate: the man for whom he carried had, quite exceptionally, given him a few coppers for food on his journey back. 'He must have been a decent fellow after all,' I said to Fu when he told me. Fu did not agree. 'Is there such a thing as a decent soldier?' he wondered. It was a contradiction in terms. However Lao Lo was once again able to carry fish for his father.

*

There were two topics which were now on everyone's lips: Japan and the communists. The Japanese, well established in their puppet state of Manchukuo, were becoming more aggressive. Our Jen Dah students expressed their feelings by looting the home and office of the Japanese consulate, tearing down from the entrance their magnificent black lacquer sign, with golden inscription, which they then dishonoured in a pit of night-soil. As for the communists, who had aided Chiang Kai-shek in his victorious march north from Canton in 1926 but then were scattered after being driven from the Kuomintang, it now seemed they had not been completely destroyed after all. Accounts of expeditions by the Central Government troops finally to destroy them reached our part of China. We heard with approval the official accounts of their suppression, for we were told they were particularly unpleasant bandits, bringing death and destruction. Nevertheless people in the tea-shops were beginning to be a little surprised that, after being wiped out several times, still more expeditions were needed. The students at Jen Dah were better informed, but they said nothing, knowing they were in real danger if even suspected of leftish thought. Then came the news that there were communists in our own province.

'There is little real danger. Szechwan is far too prosperous for communism to spread,' Artist Yü told me, when I asked him. Yet he spoke in a whisper, and held one hand over his mouth lest he should be overheard. 'They' – he did not use the word communist again – 'they are only in the arid north-east, not on the fertile plains. Anyhow the uprising has now been suppressed. The recent *la-fu* to get carriers was because the soldiers were going to fight them.'

Hsiung Wei-lin laughed when I mentioned to him that I had heard the communists were suppressed. 'Propaganda,' he declared. 'In reality the Szechwan troops have been defeated.' As a banker he had sources of information denied to most of us. Then he dropped his voice to a whisper. 'There are communist forces to the south-east, in Kiangsi province, which have been driven by Chiang from their stronghold. Who knows where they will go next? This is a wealthy province, an attractive prize for anyone who can hold it – whether our own generals, the Central Government, or the communist-bandits.'

It was indeed becoming obvious that the isolation of Szechwan must end. If war with Japan came, the Central Government would need a secure base. The lip service which the provincial governor had expediently been giving must be replaced by a more realistic relationship. Yet 'Szechwan for the Szechwanese' was a potent slogan. The rich merchants and the conservative landlords banded together as the powerful 'Szechwan Gentry' to protect their privileges which they feared would be lost if the province came under the tight control of down-river outsiders. The report that the communists in the north-east of the province were defeated was designed to keep the Central troops out; but when Chiang Kai-shek learnt that they were in fact not being held his soldiers arrived in the province without further delay.

The news was discussed by everyone. Some even doubted whether the communists existed, but were invented as an excuse for Nanking to gain control of Szechwan. Unlike the rich, the ordinary people of the Lane rather favoured more outside control. The poor, they knew, would always suffer, whatever the government, but at least Chiang Kai-shek might introduce order and restrain the local oppressors. Opinions about the communists reflected the official pronouncements. Discussing them in the tea-shop, Tailor Su, however, rather daringly asked: 'Are they really so bad? Some people say they are good.'

His companions shook their heads and looked at Headmaster Gow, whose views they respected. 'They are bad right enough,' he assured them. 'They disorganize life wherever they are. They kill and they loot. The soldiers are our real protection from them.'

'They don't protect us much,' the fish-monger was bitter.

'Only the dogs get fat on communism,' was the opinion of Old Dzen, the coffin maker. Anyone who had strayed over graveland outside a city and seen where the corpses of the poor, wrapped in old matting, are dumped, lightly covered by soil and soon found by the packs of stray dogs, knew what he meant.

It was certain that the power of the Central Government was extending into the province. Not only at New Year, but now every day there was a rash of Kuomintang flags in the Lane. On the spirit wall at the entrance into Jen Hsiao there was painted a large copy of the flag so that every time the children went in they were confronted by it. Brightly coloured pictures of the smartly uniformed leader, Chiang Kai-shek, were tacked or pasted to the wall of every shop. The Christian mission which had welcomed him as a convert took the opportunity of inviting others to follow the General into the church.

Blood-curdling pictures of communist atrocities were

stuck up on the street walls; but propaganda based on fear is a two edged weapon. People began to lose any faith they had in Chiang Kai-shek as protector when scare followed scare and fear of the communists increased. Country folk flocked to the city for protection; and many from Duliang moved elsewhere in a blind search for security from an enemy about whom so little was known. Molly's woman servant, Da-niang, had summoned her daughter from her village home, declaring that if *they* came the two of them would drown themselves in the river. Guards patrolled the streets, some in our Lane. People were searched as possible communist agents. Our students advised: 'Do not carry clubs, pistols, or lumps which might be mistaken for revolvers, lest brutal death should follow.'

The rumour spread quickly that the communist armies on the march in the south were approaching the Yangtse river; then that they had crossed it. A new panic spread, only to increase when the Provincial Governor announced, unbelievably, that he had the situation well in hand. Confronted by the anger of those who, so rightly, doubted his word, he resigned. Reinforcements were then sent to the province by Nanking. As fears began to recede, people once again wondered if the situation had not been deliberately exaggerated to enable Chiang Kai-shek to gain control.

In April, Chiang, whom we were learning to call the Generalissimo, and his wife, The Madam, came to the province. From Chungking they directed the reorganisation which was required. The Provincial Governor, who had resigned, was coaxed by his brother generals and ordered by the Generalissimo to resume his old post. He did so – but he was now Chiang's man.

Mary believed that the worst things happened in China on the best days. It was a beautiful sunny Sunday in May when we were walking with our daughter, Mei-mei, down the Lane to spend the afternoon with Molly and Deh-min.

Near the Inn of Peace and Quiet the roadway narrows, and the shopkeepers had put over it, reaching from side to side, a trellis of bamboo on which wisteria had been trained. The misty-blue ceiling of hanging blossoms had now become one of green leaves, although an occasional spray of flowers still remained. It was welcome to walk in the cool shadow under the thick foliage; but beyond it the remorseless sun seemed hotter than ever. We sat with Molly and Deh-min while their children played in the garden with Mei-mei. The orioles had arrived after their winter absence. It was joyful to hear their call once again, and see the flashes of gold among the topmost leaves of the osmanthus trees where they nested.

From the courtyard there came sounds of commotion. Lai-ma called: '_Kei lai-lo_, guests have come. Important visitor.' It was Dr David Fan, the President of Jen Dah, whose understanding of East and West made him acceptable to his staff, Chinese and westerners alike, and admired by all. He apologized to Molly for following Mary and myself to her home, but thought that she too might be interested in what he had to say. As he sat and sipped the tea, so quickly offered to him, no one could guess from his calm face the disturbing news he brought.

That morning he had been told by General Chang that the National armies had been unable to check the communists who were on the march. They had crossed the Tatu River and, moving northward, would soon be within striking distance of Duliang. The General, responsible for the safety of westerners, asked that as many as possible should leave at once. Dr Fan would give no definite advice except to assure us that as far as the university was concerned we were free to go until the danger was past; and Molly too should heed the General as communists were known to be specially ruthless in their attacks on foreigners.

After Dr Fan had left, we looked at one another in silence. Mary was the first to speak. She remembered how we had been refugees once before, fleeing from Duliang in the winter of 1926 to the safety of internationally controlled Shanghai, after anti-foreign feeling had been increased by the bombardment of Wanhsien, a city east of Chungking, by British gunboats because of interference with our treaty rights freely to navigate and trade in China's inland waters. We had met nothing but trouble while we were away: first when in 1927 Chiang Kai-shek sent his soldiers to Shanghai – the International Settlement being carefully guarded by British troops – to liquidate all communists who could be tracked down; and then later in the year we had gone to teach in Canton when a communist attack on the city was followed by its bloody repulse. I agreed: 'We should have done better to remain in Szechwan, among people we knew.'

'As always we have insufficient real information on which to base any decision,' declared Molly, for whom it was unthinkable that she should leave. It was a good idea, we all thought, that Mary, who was pregnant and planning to go a little later to a Chungking hospital, should go earlier and be safely there.

During the next few days fear once more held the people in its irrational grip; then tension relaxed when two or three government planes arrived and spent the hours of daylight flying low over the city. Little work was done, and in the Lane people stood in the roadway clapping and cheering whenever a plane passed over. The crenellations of the city walls were quickly repaired and around Duliang 'for the protection of the people' block-houses were erected, often manned by down-river soldiers. Looking back now, at the 6,000 miles epic trek of the communist armies from Kiangsi to Yenan in northern Shensi, the renowned Long March, it seems doubtful if there was any intention to attack the cities of western Szechwan. Across Wheelbarrow Lane, where the banner 'Szechwan for the Szechwaneses' had been, there was now a new one, in large red characters: 'Only Chiang Kai-shek stands between China and communism.' The people, reassured, looked to him as their protector; and the local generals, doubtless with reluctance, reconciled themselves to loss of personal power.

Mary went by the little postal plane to stay with friends in Chungking, but Mei-mei remained with me. She was now four years old, and when at the end of term we followed Mary it was also by the postal plane. It was Mei-mei's first flight, and in Chungking she saw her first real hills. Of course there were the towering mountains of eastern Tibet, but she was too young to feel the inspiration they gave to us. Scenery, in Chinese, is called *shan-shui*, a combination of those two vital ingredients, mountains and water. The two great rivers winding through the hills at Chungking so impressed Mei-mei that for the rest of the day she said nothing but 'so many mountains; so much water.' It was her first appreciation of the compelling beauty of China.

Soon after our arrival another daughter was born. In the happiness of our new domestic turmoil we forgot those who struggled with their daily problems in the Lane at Duliang. We spent the summer on the Chungking hills, to the south of the great city. They are low, and can hardly be considered cool, though the heat is tempered. Below us we could see a vast expanse of hilly country, rent by a great curve of the yellow Yangtse. When first we saw them the valleys were green with growing rice and swelling maize. Quickly they ripened to gold and then, after harvest, the empty fields became brown and red; only the tops of the hills remained dark green with conifers. It was then time for us to return to Duliang. We were the only passengers the plane could take: Mary and I with the old Mei-mei, now become Djieh-djieh, watching with pride the newest Mei-mei asleep in a long bamboo basket wedged in between us.

Although we knew that things move quickly in China,

where manpower is plentiful and life less technically complex, we were not prepared for what we saw on our return
after little more than two months absence. Molly had
warned us that we should be surprised at the changes which
had taken place. Chiang Kai-shek, establishing himself in the
province, had been for a short visit to Duliang, during which
he spent a few hours at Jen Dah exhorting those students who,
despite the vacation, had been gathered to hear him. Free
paint had been distributed to all in Wheelbarrow Lane so
that the fronts of the houses and shops gleamed brightly,
mostly white, the lacquered wood and flags adding colour.
The outside of the public convenience was again resplendent
with a coat of whitewash. Most exciting of all, to enable the
Generalissimo to visit the university by car, the Lane had
become a real road. The central paving stones were moved to
cover the drain which ran along the side. Where the wisteria
ceiling had been, the flimsy small houses, held together by
bamboo ropes, had been pushed back until the entire Lane
was of uniform width. The ruts had all vanished and the new
surface of mud and lime was grey and smooth. Wheel-
barrows, with their narrow iron-shod wheels, were now
forbidden, and had to be carried by a couple of men, unless
they were fitted with broad wheels of wood, covered with
rope or bits of old rubber tyres, which were imported to
make soles for shoes and slippers. Rickshaws had arrived in
large numbers, so that the old sedan chairs suddenly belonged
to an age that was gone.

The main gate to Jen Dah glistened with new black
varnish. From the two red lacquer pillars, one each side,
scrolls proclaimed in gold letters: 'Place the interest of the
state above that of the individual,' and 'Place the interest of
future generations above that of the past and of the present.'
New thoughts indeed for people accustomed to look to the
past with reverence, and who had learnt by bitter experience
to look after themselves and not get involved with others.

When we saw Deh-min we felt shocked. His entire head was shaven clean; and he was dressed in uniform, as were all my Chinese colleagues. There had been a conference held on Mount Omei to which Dr Fan and Gow Chung-ho were summoned. Yang Kwei-chuan, as head of the Leather School, should also have gone, but he persuaded Deh-min to go in his place. There, sitting on little stools, or standing long hours, disciplined like soldiers, the college presidents and headmasters were instructed by Chiang Kai-shek and others in the new plans for reconstructing the province, and how by a strict military discipline to fit their students to resist both communists and Japanese. The former were to be wiped out, but it was hoped a policy of appeasement might postpone conflict with the latter.

When I went to the bank I found Hsiung Wei-lin was also close cropped and dressed in a military jacket. The shape of his head, and its shiny greyness, bemused me so that it was hard to listen to what he was saying. He measured the situation by the price of rice. During the communist scare it had fallen because no one dare hold stocks; but now it was rising again, the price of all other goods keeping in step. Students paid their fees through the bank, so he was able to tell me that although the produce of 40 acres of land had been sufficient to support one for a year, now 150 acres were not enough. The cheque which I was cashing was on a Shanghai bank. I received a commission of 20 per cent as people were still wanting to send money to the safety of the International Settlement. During the panic the rate had been up to 40 per cent or more. Hsiung came round from his counter to whisper in my ear that the big man (and I could only presume he meant General Chang) had sent over a million dollars down river to a foreign bank.

Another customer approached, but Hsiung asked me to wait for a moment. When we were alone he said with a touch of reproach: 'You never found me a wife from among your students.' His need, he told me, was now getting urgent. However he acknowledged that the task of match-maker was beyond the powers of a foreigner, but wanted me to know that he had asked Bao Hsin-min's wife to assist him. She had agreed, but he could not decide whether he wanted a student who might have ideas of her own and would attempt to rule his life, or an uneducated girl who would do just as she was told, but could be little more than a servant, unable to share his life in any real way. Which should he choose, he asked me.

We saw the Wu family from time to time, but that autumn all of us were busy. Deh-min and I found that the torrent of new orders from the Ministry of Education greatly increased our work. Mary was busy with our small Mei-mei; also she and Molly had gathered round them a dozen mothers with young children to knit garments with the wool which was finding its way to Duliang from the mills of Tientsin and Shanghai.

Influenced by the new thoughts of serving China and a growing reaction against western ways, our Jen Dah students decided that at Christmas they would no longer follow the foreign custom of sending cards and giving presents to their friends. As a Christian foundation, many of our students had been to mission schools, so that they were familiar with the alien habits of their foreign teachers. Among those students who themselves were Christian, there was a growing desire to separate, if they could, the teaching of Jesus from western entanglements which missionaries in-evitably brought with them. This year they collected money for rice which they planned to give to the truly destitute. Tickets were carefully distributed and eventually the day arrived. Long before the appointed time the lame, the sick, the dreadfully diseased, with their raw ulcers and fly-covered sores, walked, shuffled or were carried up Wheelbarrow Lane.

The Jen Dah police stood guard while the great doors were opened a crack to admit those with tickets. One by one they received a measure of rice in their hempen bags. The students, however, greatly miscalculated both the number of the needy and the speed with which good news travels. Many had come with faith but no tickets. When the rice sacks were empty and the great doors closed, they were not to be denied. Voices raised in anger outside the gates shouted demands, answered from inside by equally noisy explanations. The savage beating with sticks upon the doors, the barking of the dogs attracted by the tumult, were heard down at the end of the Lane where we were with Molly and Deh-min.

The only thing to be done with a crowd is to disperse it. The police, egged on by the frightened students, drove the beggars from the gates, first with words, then with clubs. Defeated, yet still defiant, in their rags and filth, their wretchedness and great disappointment, the beggars slowly retreated. Never before had such a sight been seen in the Lane. Not even for the pressgang had it emptied more quickly, shutters gone up and doors closed.

We stood at the entrance of the alley-way, between the tailor's and the wine shop, watching them come. There was nothing we could do except retire, and with anxious pity wait until the noise had died away. Later, when Mary and I returned home, there were still some beggar children with white leprous heads in the Lane, clutching their empty bowls to their shivering bodies. A man with rotting legs was pulling himself slowly along upon a mat. Someone, whether man or woman it was impossible to say, was lying on the road, blood from the mouth staining the grey surface.

As we approached Jen Dah gates we saw a lone pathetic figure standing before them. He was tall, with little flesh to cover his bones. Despite the cold damp air he was naked save for a loin cloth, dark as his unwashed body. He stood before the closed doors, between the red lacquered pillars, and the blue hanging signs on which black characters proclaimed: The Privately Established University of Benevolence and Justice.

His arms were raised – arms that were thin and knotted, covered, like his body, with suppurating sores. Shaking his matted hair, he cried for money, for food as he hungered, for clothing as he was cold like death. From the distance it seemed from his outstretched arms as if he were nailed to the door. In him was personified all the abject misery of China's outcasts.

He cried again. From behind the barred doors came the loud voice of the gateman answering him. 'Get thee gone. This is a school. It is a foreign place where they seek not merit by good deeds. Get thee gone.'

VI

Fu Lu-chin's Indiscretions

———◇———

1936 IS REMBERED as the year of Cook Fu's indiscretions, although those without myopic involvement with Wheelbarrow Lane may think of events more decisive for China. The previous year Fu Lu-chin had been ill with fever and cough. During the summer when we were in Chungking he went back to his village for recuperation. After our return, he was not too well. He was thinner, his face often drawn; only the tufts from his nostrils remained gloriously unchanged. Each morning when he appeared to greet us, we looked anxiously at him. If he was wearing his little black hat with the button on top we knew all was well; but if a scarf was wound round his head it was a bad sign. Should the turban be white we knew he felt seriously ill.

After nursing him once or twice, Mary suggested that he needed a wife. We then discovered that he already had one, which we had not suspected: unlike other solitary men servants he had taken no occasional trips to his village to procreate sons. He promised that he would send for the woman, who lived at the home of his elder brother. He did not wish to ask the street penman to write a letter, as no one in his family could read; instead he waited to send a mouth-letter by a friend from his village who came up to trade.

Some weeks later the lady arrived. She was short and plump, with an excessively broad face, devoid of expression. When we spoke she smiled, but it was only the shape of her mouth which altered; there was no corresponding light in her eyes which were furtive, almost despondent. She understood little we said: in itself not unusual for an illiterate woman confronted by foreigners for the first time. She continued to smile as Fu led her away.

We could only imagine what Fu endured during the days that followed. Our test was to come. One morning, when doing his accounts with Mary, Fu said: 'Do you think *she* could help in the house?' Mary, a little hard pressed since the arrival of our second daughter, agreed to try her. It was not a success.

Chinese who served westerners came to occupy special positions: indispensable links between their ways and ours. Compradores employed in the big foreign business houses as intermediaries for conducting affairs in Chinese, both with staff and with other firms, were very influential, wielding great power. In a much smaller way Fu Lu-chin also had power. He had much of our money to spend; and every shop in Wheelbarrow Lane sought his custom. His was a skilled occupation. He knew what was to be done in a home with a western mistress. He knew where to buy fruits and vege-tables Mary desired. He could grow his own yeast for making bread, knew how to refine the local crude sugar, and free salt from the mud with which it was mixed. Best of all he could cook Chinese food, flavour assuaged to conform to our taste. When Mary needed ribbon or tape, he usually managed to find just what was required. Of course he got his squeeze; but as our retailer that was his right. We were spared wasting time shopping, hunting and bargaining; besides, despite his commission, we could rarely buy as cheaply as he could. It was more difficult to forgive him when he underrated our intelligence. If we had to be cheated, we preferred it to be done with pleasant finesse, not by the crude assertion that many Chinese chickens had no livers ('didn't we know?') or that our weekly consumption of eggs had risen to over two hundred. Yet if we gave way a little and were not too strict, there was always considerable give and take, part of a carefully adjusted system of human relationships, of live and let live. He frequently gave us flowers, and brought seeds and plants from his friends for our garden.

Fu must have realized that it was impossible for us to employ his wife. After several days she was still unable to make a western style bed. She smiled at the blankets and sheets, but could only fold them as she had been taught from childhood to fold her own quilt. Duliang at that time had neither piped water nor drains; and within a few hours she had broken both jug and basin of our imported crockery. To keep warm in winter we had a coal stove which stood away from the wall in our living room. A chimney, which the tin-smith had made out of kerosene tins, went up through the ceiling to the bedroom above and into the bottom of a large empty oil drum. From the top of the drum the chimney twisted about and then passed through an outside wall. This ingenious device not only kept the house warm, but an inner container in the drum provided us with constant hot water, ready to be ladled out into wash basin or bath. The final blow came when Mrs Fu emptied the bedroom and nursery waste into that inner container.

'It's no use,' agreed Fu sadly. 'I feared this. She is only fit for the country.' We knew he was greatly depressed by this large loss of face.

'But why did you marry her?' I could not help asking the crestfallen Fu.

'I didn't.'

'You didn't?' I was bewildered.

'I didn't want her. Da-go, eldest brother, married her to me. It is our Chinese custom. Our parents were dead, so he was the head. Perhaps he wanted another woman to help on the farm. He knew I didn't want her, but as his sister-in-law he did not have to pay her.' Fu gave himself confidence by

twisting the tufts from his nostrils. 'You won't see her
again.'

We pictured with pleasure Fu Da-sao on the way back to
her rural abode. Only later did we remember that Fu had
said she was only fit for the country, not that he was sending
her back.

It was about ten days later when Gow Chung-ho, the
headmaster of the Primary School, Jen Hsiao, came to our
home. After sipping some tea, he looked at me over his
plastic-rimmed glasses and, gently pulling his scanty beard,
asked quietly: 'Do you know that your cook is in prison?'

We were greatly surprised. The event had just taken place
and Gow proceeded to tell us an incredible tale. Fu Lu-chin
had apparently given his wife to the Jen Dah gateman,
whether as servant or wife we never knew. Even this
hardened and wizened old sinner had disliked the poor
woman. She was not only stupid, but wanted to sleep in his
box of a room most of the day as well as all night. She
would not wash his clothes or keep watch at the gate while he
himself had a doze. So the gateman had sold her, or 'given
her away' as Gow said, for eight dollars, although he might
have got twenty.

Gow suspected that Mary and I had never heard of the
'man-dealers' who bought and sold human beings. They
were recognized merchants in Duliang who, before it was
forbidden, traded in little girls as slaves for the larger houses.
Now they were chiefly procurers, who hovered about the
women's tea-shops such as the one where Molly found
Lai-ma. The dealers had sold Fu Da-sao to a brothel.

It was there, Gow explained, that one of the Jen Dah
students had come across her and heard her story. He felt pity
for her, and as the college gateman and my cook were involved had denounced them to the magistrate. The gateman
denied having sold her, maintaining it was in fact Fu who
had done so. Gow, always involved in the Lane's disputes,

had reason to believe, that if I would be responsible for Fu taking the woman back again, the matter would be ended 'as no one likes to waste time over such trivial affairs'.

We naturally agreed that if Fu were willing they could both continue to live at our home. Later a dejected Fu trudged slowly across the campus followed by his wife. The lower part of her face was still smiling, but there were marks where tears had run through the grime. Fu Da-sao was back once again; but her husband so obviously disliked her that he went every night to share a small room with our chemistry coolie, Lao Du, who lived in the long one-storey mud building at our end of the Lane.

There the matter should have ended, but a friend of a friend in his village came to see Cook Fu. He said that his wife had got a man at the brothel to write home to her uncle for money so that she might buy her release, saying that her husband had beaten and starved her and finally sold her. The uncle in anger had gone to the village magistrate, also a relative of hers, who had arrested Fu's elder brother as head of the family, and therefore responsible for the misdeeds of his relatives. Cook Fu may have felt that all this served his brother right, and was reluctant to send any money. He agreed that the man should take his wife back to the village as proof she was safe and had never been beaten by him.

A few hours after she left, to our amazement, she was back again, the smile still on her face, an umbrella firmly grasped in one hand, in the other her possessions tied in a small bundle. The man, so she said, had turned out to be no friend of a friend but one of the dealers who was planning to sell her again. She had slipped away while they rested at a tea-shop, and he had sought relief at a convenient *mao-fang*. The story that the cook's brother was in prison was entirely untrue: just one of those intrigues which Chinese rogues love to concoct, and which so often deceive. A suitable escort was eventually found and the woman, with presents from her husband and appropriate gifts from ourselves, went back to work for the elder brother. She was quickly forgotten, fading into the vastness of the countryside, as individuals do when no letters are written and the physical barrier of several days' journey on foot makes separation complete.

For a day or two the story was told and re-told in the tea-shop. If any pity was felt, amid the amusement, it was all for the cook, not for the woman. Yet as a result an idea occurred to Bao Hsin-min's wife, the Lane's leading matchmaker. When Mary went to buy stamps she was sitting nursing her latest child outside the post office door. Looking up, she announced: 'I've found a wife for your cook.'

It was a young woman next door, who lived in the old temple with the tutelary gods, which was now used as a small private school. The teacher, Old Scholar Fung, recited the classics to a handful of children who together repeated his words; also he taught them to write. His wife made slippers to add to their income. They had two sons: one worked with Deng the carpenter, over the way, and was the father of several boys; but the second had been taken by the pressgang and had never returned. It was his wife or widow about whom Mrs Bao was now thinking. The Fungs no longer wanted her, as by her sewing she earned scarcely sufficient for her own keep and that of her child. 'That too is good, for it is a boy.' Mrs Bao had thought it all out. 'Fu Lu-chin can adopt him – an heir all provided. So far he hasn't been very successful at begetting one of his own.'

'Fung Er-sao, Fung Er-sao,' she called loudly; and the Second Mrs Fung Junior appeared in the temple doorway. 'This is the foreign tai-tai for whom that Fu, of whom I was telling you, works.'

Mary liked her looks. 'Bright and intelligent, young and strong, in fact a second Lai-ma,' was how she described her to me.

Mrs Bao got to work and before many days the new Mrs

Fu and her child were established in the small room in our garden. I happened to see her after a hot sunny day. Fu Lu-chin, weary with shopping and his time in the tea-shop, arrived home dusty and tired. He was sitting on his low bamboo chair, his little round hat on his head, black trousers rolled up over his knees. His feet were covered by pleasant warm water in an enamel wash-basin, his eyes closed and on his face a look of content. Kneeling before him, his new wife was washing the dust from his legs with a small patterned cloth. Heaven had certainly smiled on the rascal and blessed him.

Fu invited a few of his friends to celebrate the occasion. Among the delicacies he bought with which to entertain them were two live pigeons. One was for us – he would make a pigeon pie so he told Mary. We thanked him for his thought and admired the birds in their small cage. They were plump and exactly alike. Later, by mishap, the cage door opened and one of the birds flew away. He did not rely on our generosity. 'I am sorry,' he said, when he broke the news, 'it was your bird that escaped.'

Having settled Cook Fu's affairs in such a satisfactory manner, giving peace of mind to him, and also to Mary and myself, Mrs Bao, who liked to see people well paired, continued to imagine what might happen if the single young men and nubile girls she knew were put together, especially picturing the possible effects on family fortunes. It was urgent that someone should be found for our bachelor banker; but a woman sufficiently educated to be a companion, yet not too much lest she should rule his life, was not easy to find in Wheelbarrow Lane, and Mrs Bao did not know any such girls in the city itself. At last she had a suggestion to offer. Hsiung was full of excitement when he told us the news. It was no other than the eldest daughter of Lee, Molly's landlord. We had not thought of her, yet we came to believe that the matchmaker had indeed been inspired. Miss Lee and Hsiung Wei-lin, being modern young people, had already met. Despite giggles and silent embarrassment they accepted the prospect of marriage. Mrs Bao, then sold the idea – almost literally in view of the banker's position – to Landlord Lee, who felt that his daughter was making an excellent match.

Molly was enthusiastic. When they had first come to Duliang it had almost been part of the bargain with Lee that his daughter Ruby, who in Chinese was Lu-bi, should be employed by Deh-min. She had been to a mission school, knew more English than her father, had been taught how to type and do simple accounts. She soon learnt her job, attending to Deh-min's western correspondence and drafting letters in Chinese for the tannery writer to improve and copy; those for lofty persons and government officials were always written by Principal Yang himself and were works of art, a delight to look at even if, because of their classical phrases, the recipients could not always discover just what they were about. 'She is a very good choice,' was Molly's opinion, 'a sensible girl, educated enough in the things which he understands. They will do well together.'

Lai-ma waited at the Lee's door to invite Ruby to see us when she returned from her work. She replied to our congratulations prettily and with natural ease. Her figure was short and dainty, her face curving from her broad cheek bones to her small rounded chin. Her black hair was bobbed, hiding her ears; her skin faintly sallow, but seeming pink and white compared with most of the other women who lived in the Lee's courtyards. Her plain purple silk gown, split at the sides, reached from her neck to below her knees: she was *mo-den,* in latest fashion, with stiff collar almost two inches tall. Like all unmarried Chinese girls she seemed almost curveless from head to toe. Over her tightly bound breasts swung a fountain pen on a black silken cord. She talked of the wedding, to be held after the summer, which her family would have to arrange as Wei-lin was alone in this part of the province.

Her father joined us, and showed his delight at the thought of the forthcoming wedding. He proceeded to sing his daughter's praise. Ruby was embarrassed and made her excuses, but before she left assured us that the wedding would be simple, as indeed it was compelled to be because of the New Life Movement. Landlord Lee would have liked a big splash, so he said, but we felt he was really thankful that they would have to conform and avoid those extravagances which so often led to debt.

This new Movement had been launched by Chiang Kai-shek and his wife in 1934. They brought it with them to Szechwan, introduced it to army and schools, establishing a provincial branch. The movement was designed to revive ancient virtues, to return to courteous behaviour, pure living, clean thinking and hatred of evil. In the first place it was specially directed towards the young officers in the national army, but soon we discovered it was affecting the lives of us all. Those of us who were teachers found our programme transformed. Military instructors were appointed to Jen Dah to drill our young men and teach them discipline, punishing those who did not obey. No longer could students just smile when we met them; they must stand at attention and salute. A smart officer would turn out to be a teacher colleague in the new uniform which we westerners alone could evade. A German girl, recently arrived, married to one of our Chinese staff, seeing all this, clapped her hands with pleasure exclaiming: 'How wonderful! Lovely! Just like my own Germany: all the boys and girls drilling and in uniform.'

The days for our students were strictly planned. Not only did military uniforms replace old long gowns, but bugles aroused us at dawn, called us to sing the national anthem and salute the flag as it was slowly raised. Slogans were shouted and after more drilling came breakfast, which students had to start eating at the signal and finish when a whistle was blown. Classes followed, but all through the day each moment was organized until the flag was lowered at dusk and finally bugles sounded 'lights out'. In classrooms or at lectures whenever the names of Sun Yat Sen or Chiang Kai-shek were mentioned everyone rose and stood at attention. A Youth Corps of dedicated students kept watch for slackness, promoted the ideals of the Movement, and saw that any who might be disloyal to the Leader were suitably corrected.

All this was for the elite, the officers of the army, the government officials, the students and those considered to be leaders. The Movement never really involved ordinary soldiers, never won their understanding and devotion. The common people were required to obey new rules, but without any sense of participation or understanding of the purpose for which the rules had been designed. Everyone had to be decently dressed. The sweating rickshaw puller must still run but must also wear a vest to cover his body. 'In summer there are no gentlemen,' the old proverb says; but the Movement demanded that whatever the weather a new decency must be observed. In the heat Carpenter Deng delighted to loll on a chair in his doorway, his feet on the wooden doorstep, clad only in his broad white cotton trousers and slippers. With leisured movements he liked to stroke his fat paunch and scratch his naked chest with the handle of his fan. His neighbours still laugh as they remember his rude awakening when the police condemned him for his vulgar betrayal of China's good name. Westerners walking with jackets open, or only the middle button fastened, were stopped and made to button all up. It was forbidden to walk with hands in pockets. Guards came running if they saw such a crime. In the main city streets it was permitted to walk only up one side and down the other, so shopping had to be carefully planned. A visit to a neighbouring shop might involve walking to the end of the street, crossing over, walking right down the other side, crossing over again, and then walking up to the shop you wanted, perhaps next to the one from which you started.

Wheelbarrow Lane became unnaturally clean. If even a cabbage leaf were dropped, or half-chewed sugar-cane spat on to the street, all must be picked up at once. Those delightful, but admittedly untidy, small stalls were forbidden. The street barber was watched to make sure he swept up all the hair which was scattered on the ground. Heads were still

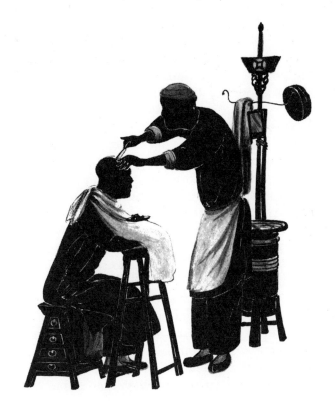

shaved, but in the summer most men and boys liked it that way. Beggars were driven from the city; our opium den, long officially abolished, was moved further out of sight; even the smoking of cigarettes in public was no longer permitted. Friends meeting in the street warned each other: 'Be careful. Old Chiang will catch you if you aren't.'

Despite its high purpose of raising moral standards and uniting the nation to face possible danger, the New Life Movement could not endure because the people saw no reason for this new behaviour which was forced upon them. In the absence of any sense of personal commitment there was no popular momentum to carry it forward. The people were not involved. Yet some things made sense: the need for simplicity in living, in funerals and weddings, for fewer dishes at feasts. In these times of rising costs, it removed the need to maintain appearances which could be ill-afforded. Popular support was given to the avoidance of luxury – to the sorrow of Ruby who, like other girls, would have liked a lavish wedding.

Landlord Lee was still with us when Ruby came running back again – but it was not to tell more of plans for her marriage. 'Piglets have come. Two piglets.' She was breathless as she had hurried from the outer gate. 'Do they belong to anyone here?'

Mary and I shook our heads. Pigs were not animals we, or our friends, were in the habit of buying. But Molly jumped up. 'They are mine. I was hoping they would come.' She went with Ruby to the gate, speaking as she went. When she returned it was with a farm woman who carried a baby pig under each arm, neatly encased in a cylinder of plaited bamboo into which it just fitted.

From the time of her childhood, when her mother had faced such economic difficulty, all waste was a sin. The New Life Movement had encouraged a sense of unease in Molly. So she fenced off a corner of the garden and planned to keep pigs. They would eat any left-over food and be ready to divide up as presents when New Year time came. She had bargained for two little pigs from this woman who had been at market. Now as they were poked and drawn out of their baskets we watched with delight as they turned up their tiny black noses, and laughed at their short curly tails, the black hair on their backs glistening with the water which had been poured over them to keep them cool.

We were charmed with them, hating to think of the inevitable changes that would occur as they grew. But Molly, despite her excitement, was already thinking of their fate. Her comment has passed into Wu family history. She expected at New Year to have eight hams to enjoy from these two little beasts. We laughed and town-bred Molly laughed too – for one never laughed *at* her, she always shared. In its trivial way this innocent mistake did as much to endear her to her Chinese relations as the birth of her sons. They no longer could subconsciously fear her; no more were they vaguely threatened by a suspicion that she belonged to a superior white race. There was no single person of that great unique family which dwelt under Heaven, the Celestial People, who did not know that no pig existed with more than two hams.

That evening passed quickly: we had to make haste. Before our campus clock struck ten we must be in our homes, or risk meeting the revolver men of the Bureau of Public Safety, sent to make sure we conformed to the new rules of Chiang's China.

★

As we threaded our way along Wheelbarrow Lane, going to the city or to visit our friends, the open shops and houses made us aware of the infinite variety of trivial affairs which make up the lives of the people who live there. Mrs Bao worried about sores on her baby's head; the guests-up-above, as they called the scampering rats, which had deserted their legitimate playground above the ceiling mats of plaited bamboo and had come down to plague Old Dzen by nesting in the coffins of all sizes which he kept ready waiting; the row of new long-spouted tin kettles, all shining and boiling away on the range at the back of the tea-shop; and the pride and the skill with which the scalding water was poured from a height on to the green leaves in the bowls; the sweet-smelling logs being carried into the carpenter's shop; Tailor Su being accused by the wife of Old Scholar Fung who declared he had stolen some of her cloth; the fish-man's youngest grandson having his first head-shave, his mother holding the babe to her breast while the barber skilfully plied his razor; the weaver, so meek and aloof to look at, loudly cursed by his wife for spending their rice-money at the Lane's brothel. There were a thousand unremarkable joys and tensions of everyday life which we observed, or about which Cook Fu took such delight in telling – details so small, yet important to him and to others, gathered as he did his shopping or sipped tea with his cronies. It was Molly and Artist Yü, as well as the banker and postmaster, who helped to merge them into a living unity for us. The outstanding events, which alone are recounted, were never isolated, apart, but bound together by all the minute unrecorded details of daily living.

For many the tea-shop, its chatter and warm fellowship, was the place where separate lives merged. The more superstitious thought of the stone lion in its brick kennel as the focus of the Lane's fortune, both good and ill. For Mary and myself it was something more distant – the towering olympian ranges of eastern Tibet, which, although only occasionally seen, yet remained a brooding presence. Among the foothills of these ice-capped mountains there lived giant pandas and musk-deer; yaks toiled there for the nomads. Chinese throughout the world ate the medicinal herbs gathered on the mountain slopes. When the sun melted the snow, the waters irrigated our rice fields, gave us the food we ate. The mountain torrents became our rivers, swollen in summer but in winter so shallow that at Duliang it was only with difficulty that junks could reach the *ma-teo*, between the south and east gates of the city.

Towards the end of summer there was a period of violent rain. For over a week water streamed in a deluge, tipped from the clouds. The downpour was wide spread, adding to the waters from the mountains, which by themselves were rarely a danger. Our river was raging; and those who lived on its banks began shaking their heads. From ancient times it had been the custom to dig out the river beds in the winter. Since the ex-bandit war-lords had come, they had collected the taxes for irrigation, but had done none of the work. For several years the beds had not been dug out, and the banks were low. The bottom of Wheelbarrow Lane, where Molly and Deh-min lived, was low lying; from the Lee's house, past their own, there was only the slightest slope to the river. The water was already trickling between the mounds of the graveland, and soon was up to the wall at the back of their house. In the morning we went through the rain to see them. The water in the heavenly well round the osmanthus trees was up to our ankles; and some of the garden was covered with shallow water. Deh-min had gone to work, but we pressed Molly and the children to return with us to the higher ground at Jen Dah. She decided to stay where she was.

That afternoon Deh-min returned early from the Leather College, which itself was on high land and secure. He had taken the road through the city, the path outside the walls being partly submerged. The water in his garden was up to his knees.

'There is really no danger,' Deh-min assured his anxious wife. 'The low land is wide between here and the tannery, so that it will be impossible to have any real depth of flood water.' They looked out from their window at the osmanthus trees across what had once been their garden. All was a brown muddy lake. The tiles of the houses were no longer grey, but sodden and black. Slowly, inch by inch, the waters were rising. They covered the side walk round the heavenly well, and then up to the steps of their own house.

Ruby Lee gave them a call. 'I'm going,' she shouted, 'I don't think its safe. The tailor is packing up his shop.' Barefoot, she waded out to the street, a stick in one hand, an umbrella in the other. She gave a final warning: 'People are moving. You had better come now, up to the high land, up to Jen Dah.'

Molly and Deh-min were still convinced that there was no real danger, besides they had their bedroom upstairs to which they could retreat. They were reluctant to take the children out in such weather, or to leave their possessions.

Landlord Lee, a broad bamboo rain-hat on his wrinkled head, was standing in his flooded courtyard calling: 'Please stay. If everyone goes thieves will come in and steal. We have a loft and you have your room upstairs.' Deh-min waded across the water to see what was happening. Mrs Lee, by paying a large price, had managed to engage a street rickshaw. Two boxes were tied on at the back, and she was nursing another. Over her head was a yellow oil sheet, from under which she was alternately encouraging and cursing the puller, who was old and weak, though eager to get his reward. He struggled at the shafts to get through the alley to the Lane, unsure of his steps in the water which was up to the hubs of the wheels.

Then Molly heard an insistent squealing from the back of the house, and remembered the pigs. They were on a raised corner of ground, but now the water had reached them. Already they were grown uncomfortably large, and were thrashing about in fear. She and Deh-min had to pull, push and half-carry them through the water towards the house door. The two boys shrieked with delight as they watched: their parents now soaked to the skin and covered with dirt.

With the exception of Lai-ma the servants had vanished. She helped them to carry possessions upstairs: the mats from the floors, the books from the shelves. The two boys rescued their toys from the cupboard. Lai-ma, her face pale and drawn, ran upstairs with pots, pans and bowls, together with a collection of kitchen utensils. When the first gentle wave of yellow water spread over the floor-boards only the heavy furniture remained there.

'The animals must go upstairs too,' Molly declared. 'It's the only way we can save them.' The pigs churned up the water as they were headed towards the staircase; but before they were up one had crashed through the balustrade and then through the floor. Eventually they were herded to a corner of their bedroom, on to an oil sheet, and were barricaded in with chairs and odd bits of furniture. Later when Molly told Mary, she shook her head sadly: 'And I always thought babies were messy, but pigs, my goodness!'

By the time it was dark the water in the ground floor was a foot in depth. It was perfectly still, no current or eddies. Yet the brown waters rose quietly, relentlessly, creeping up the white walls.

'When will it stop? Don't you think we had better leave while there is yet a chance?' Molly was suddenly frightened: they were powerless, defenceless against the invasion. Lai-ma, looking out into the darkness, abruptly announced: 'I'm going.' In the light of the lamp her face looked a sickly green. There was nowhere to go. The water during the last hour had risen again; in the courtyard it was over her waist.

They put the two boys to bed. Tired with excitement, not realizing the danger, they were soon fast asleep. Later Go-go awoke as Molly re-arranged his mosquito netting, straightening the narrow sheet over his waist. 'Mummy,' he murmured, 'it was fun getting those pigs up the stairs,' and at once again went to sleep.

It was a night of alarms. It was so black outside that they

could see nothing; but the rain sounded more gentle. They heard cries and commotion; people were calling one to another in the darkness. With a sickening crash some old buildings collapsed – and they reassured themselves that their house was new and well built. They could hear the roar of the river as it raced along in the distance. The water around them was still, unlikely to move their house from its foundations. 'Are we really safe? Will it stand the strain?' Molly asked the question for the twentieth time, and raised the small paraffin lamp, looking at Deh-min. He nodded: he believed that it would.

With a dull rumble the wall of dried mud, beyond their house, collapsed into the water. From their back window, where before there had been blackness, they could now see the distant light of the city. Holding their lamp, and straining their eyes, there was a broad sheet of water. Molly was sure she now heard, above the turbulent river, a faint lapping against their thin walls. She shivered. Man was utterly powerless against such a flood – floods such as China had known through the ages, in which so many millions had helplessly perished.

Every half-hour throughout the night she and Deh-min crept down the stairs with their lamp to mark the height of the water. Steadily it rose. In the living room their bookcase was floating. The square table had turned on its side and loomed in the distance. There were stools and buckets, also a basket such as women use as cradles for babies: they had floated in through the door which Deh-min had left open so that the water might enter freely and prevent strains on their walls.

About two o'clock they were sure that the water was rising more slowly. By three they were certain. By four it had fallen a trifle. They went back to bed and rested until dawn.

When light came they looked out on a dirty brown lake, from which houses rose. Debris was clustered about them. Floating round their own home were stools, beds and chairs, also beams from houses which had fallen in the flood. There were tears in Molly's eyes: 'All this rubbish was once valued and much of it loved.' It was not flotsam to her, but someone's possessions.

Below the window she saw an empty coffin of rough pink boards, such as is used for a child. Then another floated round the corner of the house, larger and lidless in which lay a man's body, probably waiting for burial when the flood came. Other people had been trapped and helpless just as they had been – some must have drowned. She thought of Go-go and Di-di, then trembled as she began to realise how great their own danger had been. 'At the first sign of another flood,' she told Mary, 'I shall leave and not wait for you to invite us.'

Landlord Lee came into view. He was standing on an upside down table, which he was pushing slowly along with a bamboo pole. He shoved the open coffin away from the house towards their neighbours. If, when the water went down, it was left on his land he knew there would be all kinds of complications. Molly was glad to see it go; she did not wish Go-go and Di-di to see it. Deh-min thought her too sensitive. Children should not be too sheltered. 'It does them no harm to know about death as it really is,' he said, as they watched the coffin float away, gently rocking after a final big push from Lee. 'It is natural; and they will accept it without foolish fears.'

Lee's face was wrinkled in pleasure. He was still wearing his hat, almost as wide as the square table on which he balanced, although now there was only slight drizzle. 'Is all well?' he called out. He was surveying his property. Apart from the outer wall, there was little damage. He had few complaints. 'It was snug in our loft,' he shouted up to the window. 'All crowded together. A few things have floated away, but they are mostly still in the courtyards. Heaven has sent us many gifts' – and he excused himself to gather in as much as possible before others might claim them.

Most Chinese possess the ability to cope with the unexpected. The previous evening, despite her own fears, Lai-ma had taken food, water and sticks up to the bedroom. On a stove, improvised from two enamel basins, she cooked rice in a tin. When the children awoke there was gruel for all. The floods receded more quickly than they had come. By late afternoon the ground was wet mud, but the sun was shining. The itinerant sellers of noodles and bean curd arrived, clacking two pot spoons together to attract custom. They had no need, however, to cry their wares. They were busy all day, cooking snacks for the hungry, adding red-pepper, pickles or spices to taste. That night Molly and Deh-min slept soundly upstairs; but the pigs had been moved.

The mud was depressing. It was spread everywhere and filled every corner. Mixed with it were the contents of cesspools, public and private. It had poured into the wells, and although these were emptied and washed out, for weeks Molly felt with some truth they were drinking diluted sewage. Yet no one was ill, and there were no epidemics, due without doubt to the Chinese custom, resulting from long experience, that food should be hot and only boiled water or tea should be drunk. In the sun's heat the mud dried to dust and was swept away. Floors and furniture were washed, walls repainted. The osmanthus trees still had some flowers, and in their sweet fragrance the last smell of mould was dispelled.

★

Returning from school one afternoon soon after the summer holidays, Go-go burst in with a shout: 'Something is going on in the Lees' courtyard. Come quickly and look.'

Molly went with him. In the outer courtyard, near an orange tree, a cock had been killed, its blood and feathers scattered over the ground, from which three incense sticks were standing. The thin columns of fragrant smoke mingled and rose upward in the still air. Before them, on a mat, Lai-ma was kneeling, her hands clasped together. She bowed back and forth, her head touching the ground as she repeated some words which an elderly Taoist priest was chanting for her. He stood by her side, in his long grey robe, his black wispy hair protruding in a knot from a hole in the top of his round black hat. The people who lived in the courtyards all seemed to be there, the landlord, his wife, their servants and a host of children, down to the tiniest toddler with his plump dusty buttocks exposed through his cut-away pants.

They all stood around watching.

Ruby also was there, but when she saw Molly she came and stood by her. 'They are finding a thief. Some things have been stolen. Of course all this is rubbish,' but her words were said in a manner which told Molly that she did not really believe that it was.

'But surely Lai-ma is no thief?' Molly was worried.

'Of course not,' Ruby assured her, 'but everyone, your servants and ours, must repeat these dreadful oaths, declaring that if they have stolen the goods, Heaven should strike them with foul diseases, bring torture of mind and body, a blight on their parents and children, and finally dishonour and death.'

'What was stolen?'

'Things,' Ruby's answer was diplomatic, but when she was pressed she admitted they were quilts and clothes her parents had gathered together for her marriage.

One by one the servants, men and women, knelt and repeated the oaths, all except one old woman who had been with the Lees before Ruby was born. She refused, declaring it nonsense. She was too old for such silliness; besides, through all these years as everyone knew she had never stolen a thing, not even a needle and thread. 'She must be the thief,' whispered Ruby, 'she's afraid to say the words.' Although the others accused her, pointing at her with outstretched hands, the old woman protested her innocence in a voice so loud that the servants of Artist Yü, across the road, and the tailor's little apprentices came running to see what it was all about and take part in the noisy argument.

That night the old servant packed up her possessions, had them examined by Mrs Lee, and was gone. She was not seen again, nor were the missing goods ever found. Some were sure she had stolen them, but others who knew her came to think it more likely that someone had come in from the graveland, through Molly and Deh-min's garden which, since the flood, was no longer protected by a wall. Men were now called by the landlord to rebuild it. It was plastered and painted white. Along the top was erected a beautiful pattern of tiles, so unstable that, if any thief tried to climb over, it would fall with a crash, sufficient to rouse all the dogs in the compound, whose barking would be taken up by neighbouring dogs until, from one end of the Lane to the other, everyone knew that some ill was afoot.

VII

The Banker Marries

THERE WAS TROUBLE in Duliang: money and the price of rice were the cause. In the past the army officials, their friends and relations, had bought up rice from the farmers before it came to market, using the money, it was believed, that was raised by taxation. They then hoarded the grain and released it only at a greatly increased price when the anxious people were on the verge of revolt. The price had fallen while the Generalissimo had been in the province, but since his return to distant Nanking, the wife of our General Chang had been buying up rice to store in the city. The people, fearing hunger, were exceedingly angry. There were riots, the stored rice was looted and several men killed.

At the gates of the city, conveniently placed for those who went in and out, were a number of money-changers. Before each, on a small trestle, was a wooden tray with rows of copper coins carefully packed in semi-circular grooves. They were mostly 200-cash pieces, the name a reminder of the round cash with square holes in the middle, rarely seen, but now valued very much more than the single cash which each of these old coins nominally represented. The changers gave coppers for silver dollars at the rate of the day; also the workers and petty traders could buy silver dollars with the coppers they had acquired. The number of coppers required to purchase a silver dollar increased, but popular feeling was aroused not against the money-changers themselves, but against the local branches of large Shanghai banks. The grossly ill-gotten gains of local officials and military leaders, including the profits said to have been made by Chang Tai-tai through cornering rice, were sent by them to safety in the foreign controlled International Settlement at Shanghai. All this affected the rate of exchange – always to the dis-advantage of old-hundred-names, the man in the street. Emotions were further inflamed when it was learnt that our Szechwan silver dollars were in danger of being withdrawn and replaced by paper money, a move attributed to Nanking and for which, therefore, Chiang Kai-shek was blamed.

Throughout the province dollars and half-dollars minted in Chengtu and Chungking had given financial stability. The people liked them. They did not tear or get damaged. They could be hidden in the ground; and if your house burned, as so often happened if you lived in a straw hovel, they could be raked from the ashes without loss of value. There were good ones and bad: each had to be rung against another before it was accepted. Yet all had their value, the expert money-changers skilfully deciding from the tone the number of copper-cash they would give. There were also silver dollars which came from down-river, one with an obverse of Yuan Shih-Kai being favoured. There were a few true Mexican dollars; but it was feared that all these silver coins would pass into government coffers, replaced by the paper which nobody trusted.

There were angry demonstrations in Duliang directed against the banks. Hsiung Wei-lin came to see us with a message from his manager at the city head office. He was afraid for his wife. For a few days she lived in our home, but hardly with us. She was a charming young lady, watched over by a large uncommunicative woman, who made her food, guarded her carefully, not trusting her to mix as a guest with the barbarians who had extra-territorial rights and had given her sanctuary. She kept to her bedroom; not even Djieh-djieh could entice her from it, although she herself was admitted. All we glimpsed was the expressionless perfection of her 'calendar girl' face and the seductive trousers and jacket of pale pink sateen. No wonder the bank manager, suspicious of all foreigners' morals, had sent the woman to guard his treasure, and sleep on the floor so that the bedroom door could not be opened by stealth.

Trouble, which like the wind blows where it listeth, came quite unexpectedly to Hsiung Wei-lin. Because of the feeling against the banks he had asked for a guard. His manager sent a Peking soldier from the head office. He stood at the branch door, inside our massive Jen Dah gates, fingering his revolver in its leather holster as customers, a little self-consciously, went in and out.

Cook Fu, almost speechless with excitement, brought the news.. 'He's shot someone. Shot him dead! *Ai-ya, ai-ya!*' When he was calmer we learnt what had happened. Two men were caught robbing the bank. One was shot by the guard; the other escaped but dropped the stolen dollars. 'The bag was too heavy. He could not run with it,' Fu told us. This would have been true if it had contained even a fraction of the rumoured thousand dollars, each larger than the old British half-crown, a thousand weighing well over fifty pounds. Fu deplored the stupidity of the down-river guard. 'If he had been Szechwanese he would never have fired.' The two thieves were soldiers, and as such were beyond the law, not to be thwarted except by guile. 'Now there will be trouble,' Fu prophesied – and indeed there was.

The soldier comrades of the dead man occupied a temple not far away – the one, in fact, outside the South Gate from which we had heard evening prayers as we returned from our river picnic. They threatened the bank and the lives of Hsiung and his guard, who both vanished while the bank closed. For several days groups of soldiers, their revolvers drawn, prowled around trying to find them. Responsible people must have been to inform General Chang, for he sent some of his disciplined soldiers to protect the bank, a number of them camping in the basement of one of our college buildings. Gradually the situation cleared: Hsiung Wei-lin returned and the branch re-opened, this time with a Szech-wanese guard at the door.

A strong feeling lingered about Hsiung himself. The Lane people focussed on him their dislike of down-river banks. He was also blamed because his Peking guard had killed a Szechwanese, whose thieving was completely forgotten. A wave of gossip sprang from the women: it was remembered that at the time of the flood, Miss Ruby Lee had gone to the bank and spent a couple of nights there. This was blown up out of all proportions to blacken this sensitive man who hitherto had been held in respect, a credit to Wheelbarrow Lane.

That the couple were about to be married appeared to make the situation all the more improper. His respectability was held to be shown as merely a pose, while as a banker he should have been above all suspicion. Ruby, the daughter of the worthy landlord, rich by Lane standards, should have been treated with honour. Hsiung protested his innocence: 'I slept on the bank counter. She had my room. Also old Wong Da-niang was there in the kitchen.'

Wong Da-niang, a toothless old lady, who cooked Wei-lin's rice, washed and mended his clothes, was pleased to be involved in this important affair. When questioned she said: 'Who am I to know what happened? It is not my business to interfere. I was asleep in the kitchen' – which made matters worse rather than better.

In the tea-shop it was considered that Hsiung should *den-bao*, make a statement in the newspaper. An announcement would declare the truth. It was still fondly believed that any-thing printed could not be false, even when it declared that six pigs in a litter had characters marked on their backs, reading Sun, Yat, Sen, Chiang, Kai and Shek, and in that order were born.

Hsiung said to me: 'Heaven knows I am innocent.' I believed him. He was desperate to regain the face he had lost.

Ruby stayed at home from work and hid herself in an inner room. She said to Molly: 'I could sulk to death. I am left without face.' When Molly put her arm round her and gave her comfort, she replied: 'But they are all laughing. I am shamed.'

Artist Yü shook his head. 'It is much ado about nothing. What does it matter what happened? Its common enough; in any case soon they will be married. But to want him to *den-bao*, put a note in the paper, how could he dare? You can never really be certain with women. Besides, of those who are doing the talking, who would not himself fornicate if he got the chance?'

Bao Hsin-min was more anxious to talk of his friend than sell me stamps. He came into the roadway so that we would not be overheard. 'How can he *den-bao*?' It was the question everyone asked. 'When a girl is unmarried and not kept at home anything can happen – if not during the flood, then at other times or with others.' A pack of dogs ran up the Lane, a frequent sight, their tongues hanging out, eagerly pursuing a bitch in heat. As they turned by the temple school to race over the graveland, yelping and barking, he nodded: 'Like that, any bitch out on its own . . .' He was crude but expressive.

In the tea-shop the virginity of Ruby Lee was debated, embellished by theories grotesque and frequently lewd. There was betting on whether Banker Hsiung would dare to *den-bao,* and what he would say if he did.

In due course a short notice appeared, signed by the most respected of our Jen Dah doctors. It was read aloud slowly, character by character, for scholars were scarce in the tea-shop. 'Miss Lee has been examined at her own request. She is a virgin.'

'Your-Ma-is-a-tart!' exclaimed Fish-man Lo loudly, putting the newspaper down on the table, hitting it with his fist, so that the empty tea bowls and their lids jumped in the metal saucers. 'An opportunity lost by the banker.' Then, without speaking further, he counted out coppers and handed them over to his friend the butcher.

The wedding was modern, fitting in with the times and the wishes of Wei-lin and Ruby. It lacked old-fashioned ritual: the procession of presents, the pipers, the hired ne'er-do-wells dressed in ancient regalia, carrying umbrellas, pikes and other symbols. There was no red flowery sedan chair to carry the bride from her home, reverenced, for the moment, as though she had official rank, to be dragged out weeping at the end of her journey, her head veiled by a cloth, not to be removed until bride and bridegroom, in theory, saw each other for the first time.

Landlord Lee had been to see Molly. 'I wondered,' he asked, dropping his voice and wrinkling his face in confidential appeal, 'if you would request your husband to conduct the ceremony. It would be a great honour to us. The groom unites in asking you to intercede on our behalf.'

'But why do you want him?' Molly was sufficiently western to ask such a question, It was a new role for Deh-min to play.

'His father is a well-known military official. He himself is a famous teacher at the Leather College. Also he is the father of two sons.' Molly smiled at the thought. She promised to pass on the message, bowing the grateful Lee out of her garden.

She was a little surprised that Deh-min was delighted, agreeing at once. Highly regarded in the Lane, he was fully conscious of his position. He knew it would be good for

Ruby to be married by her employer. It would restore her face.

Weddings were frequently held in the heavenly wells, or sometimes in a booth built by the side of the street to enlarge the groom's home; but Hsiung's rooms at the bank were too small, so they gladly accepted the offer of Gow Chung-ho to lend them his school, Jen Hsiao. The large classroom, which the children used for assembly, was cleaned and swept. The desks were pushed back, and the chairs, mostly ridiculously low, were rearranged in neat rows. Sixty guests · were invited, but the room was full. It was an event not to be missed. On the walls red emblems were hanging. Pots of chrysanthemums, hired for the day, gave colour to the scene, the largest blooms of all, white, yellow and brown, being arranged around the table at the top of the room.

There was loud chatter among the carefree, excited guests, all dressed in their best cottons and silks. To pass the time as they waited, they added their names with a Chinese brush-pen to a strip of red silk, decorated with hearts intertwined, which the couple would prize. Deh-min, a large red rosette on his coat, took his place behind the table, which was covered with pale green silk, lent by the tailor. Sitting by Deh-min was Landlord Lee. He had bought for the occasion new blue serge trousers to match his short blue uniform jacket, which was too small completely to hide the red knitted undergarment which was then in the fashion. A place was left for Mrs Lee who was busy feeding her latest baby at the side of the room. As the banker's parents were not able to come, Mrs Bao sat at the other side of Deh-min. It was she who had acted as middle-man for the young couple.

Bao Hsin-min, stout, full of importance, was master of ceremonies. Like all the principal actors he was decorated with a red paper flower and a large red label, pinned to his coat, on which was written his official position.

In the midst of the hubbub, Bao suddenly shouted: 'The groom enters!' There was immediate silence, then those who were still standing rushed for their seats and the noise broke out again with renewed vigour as a self-conscious Hsiung walked up to the table and stood facing Mrs Bao. He was resplendent with two broad red ribbons crossed over his chest, bunched in bows at his hips, and the latest in soft felt hats which he wore all the time and which had two red paper flowers on tall stalks fixed one at each side.

Artist Yü, after the Lane had been widened, had bought a magnificent rickshaw, with a bell which rang loudly when pressed with his foot. The little doorway at the back of the weaver's shop had been widened to let it pass through. He had engaged as a puller a young man who also helped in the garden and did other chores. Today the rickshaw was lent for the bride to ride the short distance from her home. 'Here comes the bride,' Bao Hsin-min called, while one of the teachers commenced to play the music, required at all weddings, on the small school organ, which wheezed as she worked at the pedals. Up through the guests, from the end of the classroom, with steps very measured and exceedingly slow, came Lee Hsiao-djieh. Her eyes were cast down, lavish layers of powder making her face indescribably white. She was wearing a western style white silk dress, a veil of mosquito netting and a train which was held by one of Mrs Bao's little daughters, who kept forgetting to walk as she smiled at all around her.

When the bride at length stood by the groom, all present were summoned to stand and face the picture of Sun Yat Sen, which hung below the crossed national and Kuomintang party flags at the top of the room. 'One, two, three,' called Bao Hsin-min slowly, as we all bowed our heads three times and then remained standing in silence, supposedly thinking of the founder of the Chinese Republic and the message he left that we should complete his unfinished revolutionary work.

Formal preliminaries over, the actual ceremony began, the couple bowing to each other. At the command of Postmaster Bao: 'Exchange gifts,' each in turn handed a ring to Deh-min which he gave to the other. Together they were summoned to bow to him, then to Mrs Bao and to Ruby's parents. Turning round they bowed to the guests, who bowed in return. On the table were two bright-coloured contracts, bought in the city. These Deh-min drew towards him. They were decorated round the borders with shining gold characters, wishing joint happiness and wealth, interspersed among them ducks and drakes in faithful pairs. From the barbarian west, brilliant red hearts pierced by arrows had strayed into the pattern. In a wave of activity personal seals were drawn from their cases, and in lasting red their impressions were fixed on the contracts, first by the groom and bride, then by the others at the table in witness. The sealed contracts were rolled, tied in red ribbons and presented to Ruby and Wei-lin by Deh-min who exhorted them with well-chosen words.

Despite the call from her husband demanding a speech, Mrs Bao made excuses and bowed; but Landlord Lee was eager to talk. Tears found their way down through his wrinkles to drip from his chin as he spoke of marriage, of his own productivity, and the life that his daughter was now going to lead.

At last it was over. Chairs and stools were pushed aside, round tables, some from the school, others borrowed from neighbours, were brought in from the yard; and after the usual arguments about who should sit where, the guests settled down. The feast was about to begin. The steaming dishes were brought on large wooden trays, and also a large wooden tub of rice, from the Inn of Peace and Quiet where they had been prepared. The groom, encouraged by Hsin-min, made a brief speech, thanking the guests for their presence, regretting the poorness of the food which he had provided. The bride, who had left us, returned in a silk gown of rose-red, cheeks now rouged, lips also bright scarlet. There was toasting and laughter, the couple going from table to table to drink at each a small cup, full of the warm yellow wine.

Each guest was urged to say something, and many responded. The good food and wine made even dull words seem witty. When it seemed as though proceedings would drag, it was discovered that Deh-min had provided a surprise. A puppeteer from the city had arrived with his equipment tied to his back. This he unpacked and slowly set up in the school yard.

The excitement was great. The low chairs and trestle stools were dragged from the classroom and arranged at one end of the yard, with two formal square chairs for the groom and his bride in the centre. Those who were elderly were persuaded to sit, although a number were still at the tables where servants were hastily piling the empty dishes and bowls on trays, which they carried away on their heads, hoping to return from the Inn before the show started. Everyone, young and old, was anxious to listen, although they knew every word that was going to be spoken. There was talking and joking; Mary and I, and perhaps Molly, must have been the only ones present who felt any impatience at the interminable time the man took to set up his booth. The children peeped through the curtains to see that the puppets were all there, and kept running to their ba-bas and ma-mas to tell what they had seen.

At last the old ladies with their tiny feet, and the venerable grandfathers to whom respect must be shown, were settled and the newlyweds perched on the edge of their uncomfortable high seats of honour. A final few words from Bao, a peep through the curtains by the puppeteer to make sure that all was ready, and the show began. First the puppets appeared, one by one to wish, with a bow, long life and joy to

Wei-lin and Ruby. This brought delighted applause and the children shouted the name of each as it popped up its head.

The tale, when it started, was the familiar one of poor Widow Wong, who had an only son to support her. He gathered firewood, and one day in the forest met a tiger which, to the joy of the children, devoured him. In the picture which Yü Tse-tan drew he has shown this sad encounter. The widow, with no one to support her, complained to the magistrate who ordered the tiger's arrest, sending yamen runners to catch him.

In due course the tiger was brought to court. As he listened to the magistrate tell of his crime, he hung his head in great shame. When ordered to look after the widow for the rest of her life, the tiger agreed. 'See, he is bowing his head to show that he will,' an excited small boy beside us exclaimed.

The tiger was true to its promise. Every day when the old woman opened her door there were eggs, meat or gold coins. She soon became rich and then, naturally, very respected. She died at a great age and was buried; but strange sounds came from her grave – sounds so realistic that the little boy shivered. It was the tiger who mourned, until finally it wasted away.

The last scene was in the world of ghosts, before the spirit judge, who laboriously explained that in reality it was the spirit of the son that had entered into the tiger. His filial devotion to his old mother was so strong that it did not die with him, but found means of continuing after his death. 'And so, much loved small friends, we must all love and care for our parents.'

The final moral was echoed by Gow Chung-ho, who had joined us. 'Is it not so?' he asked the little boy, putting his hand on his shoulder. Then turning to us: 'You know who this is?'

'One of the Bao children,' we rightly guessed.

'The prize fly-killer of the nursery division!' The headmaster announced the full title with all the dignity that it deserved. His school, like others in Duliang, indeed throughout China, was trying to educate the children, and through them the people, in hygiene and awareness of their responsibilities as citizens. Every year 'when flies are about to prosper, a Spring Fly-perishing Meeting is held'. The first in Duliang was organized by the Y.M.C.A. which offered tickets to their cinema for every ten flies caught. Things had moved greatly since then. Slaughtered flies were no longer counted but weighed. We asked Bao Di-di how many he had destroyed to win his prize. 'Many, many,' he told us, 'so many they could not be counted.'

'Many envelopes full,' the proud Gow explained, 'more than anyone else.' Despite this onslaught the flies in Wheelbarrow Lane seemed as plentiful as ever: on the freshly washed vegetables, on the sugar cane cut ready for chewing, covering the sliced melons, buzzing round the butcher's shop, on the heads of the children.

'A final notice! A final notice!' Bao Hsin-min called, trying to make himself heard as the wedding party was ending. 'Don't forget that the new couple will be sleeping tonight at the bank, within the Jen Dah gate.'

'As I have three sons I was asked to make the bed,' his wife added amid laughter. 'I was happy to do it, but please understand I take no responsibility for the results.'

'We shall have to go,' Molly whispered to Mary as we left. 'I hate it, but Ruby will be disappointed if we don't.'

Later that evening we went to the bank. Wei-lin's austere room was transformed. The walls were newly washed white. Presents were placed in prominent positions where their donors could see them. On a low table, before a small mirror, were bottles of perfume and imported cosmetics. At each side of the mirror, red wooden hearts were hanging, on which were painted young men embracing their lovers: the encouraging gift of one of Ruby's girl friends.

The large wooden bed with its curtains and small fitted drawers was gorgeous. It had flowered folded quilts and embroidered pillows. A new Ruby, on whom the aura of old China had fallen, was sitting on its edge, as brides have always sat, condemned to be silent, showing neither amusement, tears or anger, while guests touched her and teased her with Rabelaisian licence. Yet Ruby at heart remained modern. Her own laughter would keep breaking out, but she covered her face to hide it. When her hands were pulled away, her smiles were suppressed. 'You shame me,' she kept exclaiming. 'Don't laugh at me. I am ashamed.'

Wu Go-go and our little Djieh-djieh had demanded a peep at the bride in her room. We had taken them with us, glad of the excuse they provided for leaving early.

For days afterwards the children played weddings. Djieh-djieh, of course, was the bride with a tablecloth train, which Go-go dutifully carried. Once she called to Fu Lu-chin, who was watching: 'Look, Cook Fu, I'm a bride!'

'Indeed you are not,' he vigorously replied, twisting one of his tufts. 'If you were a bride you wouldn't be talking so much.'

The real bride and Hsiung Wei-lin soon left us. They had neither forgotten nor truly forgiven the Lane people for the treatment they received before they were married. Hsiung went to manage a bank in Santai, several days journey away: for him a welcome promotion, for us a sad loss.

After the wedding the rest of the year passed very quickly. We were going on leave. That meant extra classes to be taught, the bustle of packing and travel arrangements, and many invitations from friends wishing to bid us goodbye. Yet during that time two events occurred which were decisive for China.

The first was then a startling new influence. The government established at Chengtu, the provincial capital, a broadcasting station, bought (it was said) second-hand from Britain. It provided a new dimension undreamed of by the great sages whose words had swayed the Middle Kingdom throughout the long centuries. It was to have a profound effect on the whole of the country, helping to unify it as never before, teaching the millions of people to speak the same language (not only write the same characters), causing the

people of Wheelbarrow Lane to be aware of their *tung-bao*,
their brothers and sisters who dwelt throughout the length
and breadth of the land.

All the big shops had receivers which played at their
loudest. The same girl was singing, or the same person
speaking, from every one, the voices rising to a piercing
crescendo as one passed each open door. There was a new
uniformity, so different from the days of gramophones,
when noisy records, all different, burdened the air in wildest
discord, frequently augmented by pipers or drummers who
were doing their best to attract customers to a particular store.

In the shops of the Lane there were little boxes to which
sound was relayed. Among the songs and the Chinese music,
the Generalissimo himself sometimes urged us to gird up our
loins and loyally accept new responsibilities. We were
constantly warned of the communist menace, and the
possible danger of war with Japan. Although if war should
come it was believed in the tea-shop, it would affect the down-
river people, but hardly ourselves in the far west of China.

There was a growing anti-Japanese feeling, which the
broadcasts encouraged. A party of Japanese foolishly
attempted to visit Chengtu, where an angry mob killed two
and wounded another. The provinces competed with each
other in presenting the Generalissimo with military planes.
Although 'voluntary', Deh-min like other Chinese teachers,
found that his 'free gift' was deducted from his salary. The
radio urged everyone to greater efforts by telling of the
great sums other provinces had already raised. The people
of Wheelbarrow Lane were also encouraged to prove their
patriotism by giving more than their neighbours, the amount
each person gave being written on a board which hung in the
tea-shop.

An educational exhibition came to Duliang to describe
modern warfare. The radios blared all day giving instructions about the precautions to take if air raids should happen.

Buzzers wailed at the end of the Lane, a signal for all to take cover, although many, to the dismay of the guards, rushed into the streets to watch the planes flying low, pretending to be Japanese. Previously people had been disturbed by the stories of the communist menace; now there were scares about the Japanese and their agents. Then in the midst of all this came the startling news: Chiang Kai-shek had been captured.

That the Generalissimo should have been siezed by the communists amazed us. We were alarmed at this proof of their daring and growing strength. Then, more unbelievable still, came the news that the communists were not directly involved. He had been kidnapped by national troops whom he had failed to support against the Japanese in 1931. They were anxious days in Wheelbarrow Lane, as in the rest of China. Chiang, we imagined, stood between us and the communist danger. He was also our sole protector against the Japanese. If anything happened to him, on whom could we count?

Those whose knowledge was greater told us how all the time while Chiang had continued his war against those whom he called the communist-bandits, Japan had been tightening her grip. A cry 'Chinese must not fight Chinese. Unite to oppose Japan', had been heard from students, and some Chinese leaders. Kuomintang soldiers in the north heard this cry and understood its meaning. They responded to a similar call from the communist ranks that they should stop fighting each other and prepare for the war with Japan.

Chiang had flown to Sian to put an end to this nonsense, but officers of the North-eastern army restrained him. Some wished to kill him, but his life was spared at the insistence of Chou En-lai who had come from the communist stronghold to intercede. The communist leaders, Mao Tse-tung and Chu Deh, realized that only Chiang Kai-shek could at that time command sufficient support to lead a united country against the national enemy. The price of his life at Sian was that he should end his anti-communist campaign and prepare for the inevitable struggle against Japan. This was indeed a decisive event.

It was during the evening of Christmas Day, 1936, that news came of Chiang's release. The Lane, like the rest of Duliang, went wild with excitement. Strings of crackers were let off, and parades marched here and there that night and next day. The tea-shops were buzzing with talk as people gathered to try and discover what it all really meant. We had been with our children to a farewell Christmas party with Molly, Deh-min and their two boys. On our return home there was a note in English from one of my students: 'Besides the happiness of Christ's birthday, here comes another happy news. The Generalissimo is free again. Long live our leader!'

A few days after this double celebration we left for Chungking, there to catch a larger plane for Hong Kong. What a time to be leaving not only my students and fellow teachers, but also our friends in Wheelbarrow Lane. We felt like deserters, for we were anxious to share in the events which we knew must be coming. But we westerners are geared to a society in which detailed plans, once made, must be followed. The Chinese, less rigid, much freer, are more able to change all arrangements at a moment's notice, often to the disruption of others who may be involved. They are not limited by office hours, time-tables and clocks. Our planes and our sailings were booked; we had a house already rented for a year in England, where also we were hoping another child would be born; we were neither rich enough, nor sufficiently flexible to throw it all over. To comfort ourselves, we said to each other, that a year would soon pass. We should be back again before any big changes could happen which were likely to affect the people of Wheelbarrow Lane.

VIII
The Coming of Napoleon

THE REVEREND JOHN HARLASS was right when he told Molly that China was the land of the unexpected where best endeavours are so often brought to naught. It is rarely possible to make plans far ahead, so people learn to live for the day, dealing with circumstances as they arise. While we were on leave in England, the Japanese struck their decisive blow at Marco Polo Bridge, outside Peking, on July 7, 1937. We followed the war news in the British Papers, and decided, when the year was over, that I should return to China alone. It was already January when I was flying from Hong Kong to Chungking.

In the seat next to me was a friendly young man: a thoroughly westernised Chinese, who had spent several years as a student in the United States. He was in foreign-style clothes, which looked very expensive and designed to impress. He had a frank open face and was anxious to talk. His name, he told me, was Napoleon – Napoleon Chen, 'But usually the folks call me Nap.' He was visiting relations in Duliang, although his home was Shanghai, 'But it's no use going there because of the war.'

The war was a terrible nuisance as it interfered with Nap's plans, although he himself felt very little involved. He had very much enjoyed his time in the States: 'Of course it is busier, and very different from our dull China,' he confided. 'I enjoy the entertainment of western culture,' he glanced down at the tennis racket lying at his feet. 'The winters didn't bother me at all, but the snow did at first. I did far more swimming over there than in Shanghai, because the pools were so many and very well heated.'

As we continued to talk I was aware that he was watching a Chinese girl who was sitting alone a few seats away. She was young, her short black hair waved in the latest Hong Kong fashion, slim in a silk brocade dress, the red of her lips startlingly bright against her pale brown cheeks. She was so lovely to look at that I did not wonder that Napoleon's interest in my conversation was waning fast. With a half-murmured excuse he left me and went to the empty seat beside her.

The girl looked at him, and then with a pout, such as Chinese girls are particularly adept at making, turned abruptly away, gazing intently at the mountains below us. Less than half an hour later they were deep in conversation and laughter, while I was left to reflect on one of Principal Yang Kwei-chuan's balanced sayings which came to my mind: It is natural for youth to have its romance, just as age gets consolation from Buddha. They again sat together in the small plane to Duliang, but before we touched down Napoleon had introduced me to Sylvia, and had accepted an invitation to play tennis on the grass courts near my home at Jen Dah.

It was good to be back, to be welcomed at home by Cook Fu, his wife and son, to return to my students and work, to see again Wheelbarrow Lane, so familiar but now greatly changed. It had gone into mourning: every piece of white plastered wall was painted with soot and lime lest Japanese planes be attracted. The throngs of people also surprised me. It seemed as though the population of Duliang had doubled in my absence; and that indeed may have been true. Certainly the Lane was now a crowded thoroughfare, leading not only to Jen Dah and the farms beyond, but to new simple dwellings erected where previously there had been rice fields. Refugees, many of them young, were pouring in from the coast, fleeing before the Japanese armies. There were men and women in modern clothing, men in shorts and open-necked shirts, women in gowns with short sleeves which would have shocked an older generation, yet mostly still with the high necks and collars which modesty demanded.

Many universities and schools in the coastal provinces had been destroyed. Their students travelled great distances across China to continue their education – this great trek westward being one of the outstanding events of our times. New colleges and schools were established in the West, although many students crowded into those which already existed. Jen Dah was overflowing, so that two shifts were needed, refugee teachers caring for their own students after our own swollen classes were finished. On our campus temporary buildings were hastily being built to house and teach still more refugees. The effect of new ideas sweeping in to Szechwan was enormous. Almost overnight Wheelbarrow Lane had been jolted through a decade into the present. The changes were so rapid that many people were bewildered, and had no clear understanding where this confrontation with coastal influences was leading them.

The greatest of joys on my return was to meet Molly and Deh-min once more; but so much had happened to them that only gradually was I able to piece together their story. Molly had made a new western friend. To use Landlord Lee's words, she had again been productive. At the Jen Dah clinic, to which she went, she met Stella Bell, a Canadian nurse, older by several years. Stella was a trifle taller than Molly, with light hazel eyes. Her hair, usually hidden beneath her cap, when freed hung golden, without curl or wave, around her head. They were drawn to each other at once. Stella had the freshness and wellbeing which Molly, at that time, was greatly needing. She became a frequent visitor at Molly's home and shared in making ready for the new baby. Soon they both knew all that was worth knowing of each other's lives.

The baby was born in the small Jen Dah hospital; but before Molly went there Deh-min made sure that, in case of need, milk was available. Since Wu Di-di was born the pattern of life in Duliang had changed, and more people were using cow's milk. There was now a cow-man who had a straw shed on the graveland behind their house. By lending him sufficient money to buy another cow, Deh-min en-

sured that there would be milk. Landlord Lee went out to inspect. 'A cow with very big breasts,' he reported to Molly in English. 'Very good. Very nice.'

The walls of the hospital ward were decorated with pictures of babies, all fat, all rosy, some dressed, but all posed to show they were obviously male. Despite this encouragement the new baby, to Molly's great joy, was a daughter, a thousand ounces of silver, or, very formally, Wu Han-er. A few days following her birth they were both carried home on the hospital stretcher, with its covered top, and put to bed, watched over by Lai-ma, who was delighted to have another baby under her care.

A day or two later, Molly was still resting in bed, propped up by pillows, her thin face pale, but with gay colours flashing on her bed jacket, sent from Hong Kong by her sister-in-law Yuk-laan, on which flaming embroidered dragons trod the clouds and sported with the red sun. She was feeling content and perfectly happy. She could hear her two boys at play. Deh-min was quietly standing near her, admiring his daughter lying asleep in the crib which all their children had used. He still liked to dress in western-style clothes. He turned to her and they smiled: there was no need for words. It was Deh-min who broke the silence. 'We're going to have visitors,' he told her, and reaching forward touched her hand with his.

There had been a letter from Colonel Wu. After the fall of Nanking he moved with other officials to Hankow, but pressure from the Japanese was such they could not hope to remain there for long. The aged President, Lin Sen, and those departments of government less involved in active affairs were already establishing themselves in Chung-king, which had been selected as China's war-time capital. The Colonel's house in the Shanghai French Concession was still safe.

In 1842, after the first opium war, Shanghai had become

one of the treaty ports which China was compelled to open, where foreigners could live under their own government. The British and American sectors of the port had united to become the International Settlement, while the French Concession had remained apart. In these oases of foreign privilege, wealthy Chinese like Colonel Wu could live relatively secure, safe from the uncertainties of Chinese rule. Outside the boundaries was the Chinese municipality, which the Japanese now controlled. No one could guess how long the treaty port itself would be able to remain intact.

Deh-liang, Second Brother, and his wife, Yuin-shao, were at present remaining in the family mansion, but it was better for Old Mother and Deh-chin to get away from Shanghai. 'They will naturally live with us,' Deh-min expressively held out his hands.

'Of course,' nodded Molly, her happy dreams shattered. 'Where else could they go?' They were flying from Shanghai to Hong Kong and then, like so many others, would come to the security of the far west. They were to expect them the following week.

Left to herself, Molly looked at the crib. 'Wu Mei-mei,' she said half aloud, 'you are not only Chinese, but, like your two brothers, you are most certainly a member of the family Wu before you have any great chance of being my very own baby. Where shall we put them?' – and in her mind she rearranged her home and started re-planning her life.

Next day was warm, with bright winter sun. Molly felt a new hope. When Stella Bell came to see her patient, she found her full of smiles.

'Is it the sunshine, or the daughter, or perhaps both?' she asked by way of greeting.

'News!' replied Molly. 'My mother-in-law is coming to live with us.'

'Oh, my dear, how can you possibly manage?' Stella was dismayed.

'It's going to be fun,' Molly's eyes were sparkling at the thought of playing a new game. 'I am going to show Old Mother Wu that an English girl can be just as good a daughter-in-law as any Chinese.'

Later, she said as much to Deh-min. 'You must help me, and tell me what to do. You'll see, I'll be a good daughter to Old Mother.'

'Yes, I will help,' agreed Deh-min, then added: 'By the way, workmen are coming today to start making an air-raid shelter. The land is so low, and the soil so sandy, that it will need bricks and stones. It will take a great deal of making.'

'And that,' laughed Molly when later she told Stella, 'is real filial piety. He wouldn't make one for me, although I said we should have one. After all it is part of the tradition: he can always get a new wife, but never another mother. Yes, this is China. Now hand me my Chinese daughter.'

When the time came for the arrival of Old Mother and Deh-min, Molly was not feeling fully recovered; but when mother-in-law comes to stay, personal aches and weariness must be forgotten. She looked around the living room with a nod of approval. The furnishing was simple, but everything was tidy. In a large pale-blue bowl some narcissi were nodding, like the water fairies after whom the Chinese had named them. By the bookcase, some sprigs of *la-mei* – chimonanthus – were set in a tall Kang Hsi vase, their wax-like yellow blossoms fragrant and lovely on the bare branches.

There had been a slight struggle over the bedroom. There were only two rooms upstairs: their largish one, and a smaller one in which the two boys slept. Deh-min had wanted them all to crowd into the smaller room and leave theirs for Old Mother and Deh-chin, who would attend to the old lady's wants. Molly protested that this was unrealistic; and, rather unwillingly, Deh-min let her have her way. They had hastily got Carpenter Deng to make bunks, so that the two boys could sleep in their room. Mei-mei had her cot. The big room was crowded, but Molly was right: the smaller one would never have done.

In the little room there was now a magnificent Chinese four-poster, which Deh-min had bought in the city. They had also two new pillows and a quilt, padded with waste silk, to which was stitched one of Tailor Su's bright flowered covers. Old Mother would not be dishonoured when she slept there in state. Against the wall they had placed Molly's low dressing table whose mirror helped to make the room light. As you went in through the door you could see the reflection of a bunch of camellias on the high chest of drawers, and of the red and gilt lacquered board round the top of the bed. When the room was arranged, Deh-min felt happy.

Deh-min had gone to the airport to bring back his mother. For her he had borrowed Artist Yü's private rickshaw. He would call street ones for himself and his sister. Molly sent Lai-ma to stand at the end of the alley, with instructions to come quickly to tell her as soon as she saw the rickshaws approaching.

'*Lai-lo, lai-lo,* they are coming.' Lai-ma came running and then back to the Lee's main gate to help with the luggage. When Molly got there she saw four rickshaws, not three. Her heart gave a leap. She could not suppress a cry of amazement. Getting out of the first, coming towards her, was laughing Yuk-laan – slender Yuk-laan, eyes sparkling, a long grey coat over her pale pink silk gown, as lovely and fresh as if she had stepped out of her Hong Kong home a moment before, instead of spending long hours in the air.

The two women were in each other's arms in a moment. Molly was crying, but Yuk-laan would not allow her to linger. 'Come, we must help Old Mother,' she whispered. Together they assisted her out of the rickshaw. Deh-chin was already there. She was even more slender than Yuk-laan. ('No wonder they think all we western women are big boned, large hipped and gross,' Molly had said when describing the meeting to Stella.) Deh-chin's face, despite her broad forehead, was absurdly like Deh-min's. 'Welcome, welcome,' everyone was saying at once. The people who lived in the courtyards gathered round the doorway and joined in the chorus. The servants untied the luggage while Deh-min paid the hired pullers.

It was like the experience in Shanghai all over again. The thought of meeting Old Mother again had filled Molly with apprehension; but she was so tiny and fragile that when they actually met fear gave way at once to love and respect. She seemed a little pathetic as they led her into the house and sat her down in the most comfortable chair, while Da-niang and Lai-ma bustled about getting tea and refreshments. Mother Wu looked about her enquiringly. Molly had forgotten how thick were the lenses of her glasses and how lost was the expression they gave to her face. When the two boys were led in to pay their respects, she smiled at them, although Go-go, despite the combined efforts of the family, refused to bow his small head. Lai-ma brought Mei-mei to be admired.

The tired old lady was soon safely on her bed, wrapped in the warm padded quilt. Molly standing beside her, reached out her arms and took the small wrinkled hands in her own. 'I am, as you know, ignorant of many of your ways, but, as you did in Shanghai, you must tell me what I should do. This is no longer my house: it is yours. Anything you want I shall try to do for you. Please be patient and forgiving.'

'You are a good daughter, though not of our people.' There was a pleased smile on Old Mother's lips. 'You now eat rice, and so are learning our ways. It is good for me to be here. Tomorrow we may talk, but tonight I am tired.' Then, as Molly was leaving, she called her back, revealing her thoughts and possibly her fears: 'The two boys have eyes and hair like our own. That is good.'

'You shall teach them and help me to train them in proper Chinese ways.' Molly spoke with a sudden warmth of feeling, forgetting her fear that Old Mother might thoroughly spoil them.

'Now be off to bed yourself,' interrupted Yuk-laan with firmness, leading her to her own room. 'You, as you "sit for a month" still need to rest.' Molly unexpectedly tired, was glad to lie down, but wanted to know how it came about that Yuk-laan had given her this delightful surprise by coming with the others.

'I am Eldest Brother's wife,' to Yuk-laan this obvious reason was quite sufficient. 'We knew it would be difficult for you: Old Mother coming to live, the baby just born, the upset of the war. Deh-chin is willing but has little experience. Besides, I wanted to see you again.' Until Mei-mei was fed and put to sleep for the night, the two women chatted at the gate of the dragon.

During the next two weeks, before she returned to Hong Kong, Yuk-laan took charge of the house. She settled Old Mother, she saw that Molly was thoroughly rested, she helped Deh-chin to meet a family of old friends who had also fled from the coast. Molly was learning that although the Chinese family meant widened responsibilities and some loss of freedom for each individual in it, yet there came in return a sense of security, and the assurance of help, when help was most needed.

When I first met the Old Tai-tai, she had already been settled in Duliang for some months. She was just as Molly described her: a small, rather shrunken lady, old by Chinese standards rather than in years. She was in black silk, from the small hat on her head, down to the shoes on her tiny feet. My first impression, when we were introduced, was one of the bewildered look her thick glasses gave her – entirely deceptive, I quickly discovered. She did not have much to say to me apart from the traditional courtesies, perhaps because I was western and spoke Szechwanese, instead of the pure Pekinese, with which she was as familiar as with her own Shanghai dialect. She was sitting near the window, from which she could see into the open courtyard with the osmanthus trees and watch the people there as they did their work. She could see the coming and going of workmen who had long finished the air-raid shelter in the back garden, but which now they were covering with a great mound of sand. This was brought on wheelbarrows which squeaked and groaned as they were shoved and pulled through the safe-gate-of-escape in the back wall. Near her were her bowl of tea and her water pipe. Deh-chin, sitting on a stool, was rolling spills from rough unsized brown paper, ready skilfully to kindle a smouldering spark when her mother wanted to smoke a ball of the fine shredded tobacco. Deh-chin spoke excellent English and, like one of my own senior students, was open and easy to talk to. She was *mo-den,* that transliterated word which applied not only to fashionable dress, but also to ideas gained from the western world.

Old Mrs Wu must have missed her own Shanghai mansion, where she had every domestic convenience for cooking and washing, and a car at her service. Only once, Molly said, did she ever complain, and that was merely to shake her head and declare: 'I never really knew there were people in China who still had to live like so many do here – just as our ancestors did.' Perhaps she was stunned by the war and the changes in her life; or it may have been her Chinese ability to take life as it came, bending like the bamboos in the wind, adjusting to new circumstances without useless complaint or exhausting struggle. She was happy to watch the two boys as they played when they came in from school, and told them stories to keep them around where she sat. Lai-ma frequently gave her Mei-mei to hold or to lull to sleep; she, with Deh-chin and Molly, conspiring to anticipate her wishes as far as they could.

When the warm weather came, Old Mother frequently sat at the end of the alley in a bamboo arm-chair by Tailor Su's shop. She watched the people as they passed by on the Lane, happy when as frequently happened she saw others who had come from the coast. They would stop to talk in their own Shanghai dialect, not understood by the people who normally lived in Wheelbarrow Lane. No one seeing her there would imagine she once successfully controlled a wealthy household in the French Concession and, but for the war, would be doing so still.

Once or twice she told Deh-min and Molly: 'Our good fortune is great, very great.' She would then repeat a story she had heard. Few had been able to come inland by air. Those who travelled westward for part of their journey by ship had many of them been compelled to stand on crowded decks for a number of days and nights, lying down for brief spells by turns. They had days of starvation and thirst. Most unhappy of all were those who had been forced to flee overland on foot. Children were lost; some were abandoned as they themselves could not walk, nor could their parents find strength to carry them, especially over the snow covered mountains. One woman, who frequently talked with Old Mother, had left with nine children, but arrived in Chungking with only one. Two had been lost on the way through illness, the rest in a boat accident in the current off Ichang at the entrance to the gorges. Now the last one had died of sickness in Duliang. Some refugees had spent long hours cramped in buses, unbelievably overcrowded. There had been breakdowns, accidents and hair-breadth escapes, in addition to adventures with robbers who stole even the few possessions the poor people carried. 'Yes, we are fortunate. Our luck is good.' Old Mother was reconciled patiently to wait until the wind stopped blowing or changed its direction.

From time to time Napoleon Chen, who was still living with his relatives in the city, came to Jen Dah to play tennis.

Sylvia arrived soon after he did, in a luxurious rickshaw, black varnish shining, with two chromium lamps and copper mudguards, all highly polished. However bright the sunshine, the hood was raised and the rain-apron fixed high. It was impossible to see her until she alighted. The tennis she played was exceedingly pat-ball, which Nap could never have tolerated but for his obvious infatuation. Cook Fu squeezed oranges and limes to prepare drinks, which he lowered in a basket down our well to be cooled until they were wanted; but to me he would shake his head and murmur enigmatically: 'No good, no good. Nothing good will come of this.' I put it down to old Chinese morals; but perhaps he knew more than he was prepared to tell.

Nap said one day: 'I have been to see some friends of yours down the Lane. Colonel Wu has come on a visit.'

This was news to me; but I had not seen Molly or Deh-min for some time. I was exceedingly busy as Jen Dah was attempting to cope with the influx of students who, for the most part, had walked across China, fleeing from their colleges as the Japanese armies advanced. 'How do you know Colonel Wu?' I asked, for although I had told Deh-min about meeting Napoleon Chen on the plane from Hong Kong he had given no indication that the name was familiar.

'My father works in the government too – but, of course, he is not really important like the Colonel.' He spoke modestly of his father's status, but whether truthfully or only politely, I could not tell. 'They were at school together. I was ordered from home to call and pay my respects.'

It was partly curiosity which made me do likewise. I had heard so much about Colonel Wu from Molly that I wanted to meet him. He had, I knew, recently moved to Chungking from Hankow. As far as I knew, this was his first visit to his wife and family in Duliang.

On the Lane, by the wineshop, there was a military car surrounded by children who were trying to touch it, a soldier on guard fruitlessly attempting to thwart them. The Colonel was not at home. He had gone across the road to visit Yü Tse-tan. The two men, so different in everything else, had found common ground as lovers of birds. Molly took me over to meet him, telling me how the reputation of her father-in-law soon spread so that sellers of birds had flocked to the house, carrying their wares in all manner of cages. In fact there had been little privacy since the Colonel arrived. With him, apart from the driver, were four soldiers who acted both as servants and guards. One was responsible for the birds, bringing two in their cages, which they had held on their knees during the journey. Where the men slept Molly never enquired – perhaps in the car, perhaps in the kitchen, perhaps on the living room floor. She was learning that there were many things about which it was better not to ask: most problems if left to themselves were resolved. There was always a guard or two in the kitchen, seeing that the food was cooked as the Colonel liked, while the others stood look-ing in through the windows, ready to obey any orders that might be given. They respected Old Mother, and were polite to Deh-min. They played with the children, liked to nurse Mei-mei, but ignored Molly entirely.

The Colonel, short, thick-set, a much older edition of Deh-min, was smart in his uniform. He was bareheaded, whistling and making encouraging noises, with his nose pressed to the bars of a bird cage. It was some moments before he saw us, then, clicking his heels to attention, held out his hand as Molly told him who I was. 'Ah! a fellow countryman of my small son's wife,' he said pleasantly. 'From the land where pigs have four hams. Tell me, is it really true that there are pigs like that in your country?' – and he gave an emphatic wink at Molly, who laughingly assured him that it was perfectly true.

Artist Yü and he had been up in the early morning, delightedly persuading their birds to fly from cage to cage.

One cage was hanging on a tree in the courtyard, the other held up by Wu. One of the Colonel's birds readily flew from a strange cage back to its own; but two of the Artist's had been trained to exchange cages when the doors were opened and the correct encouragement given. The conditioned birds did not choose freedom, but preferred the security of their prison walls.

The Colonel was anxious to speak of the war. When Yü Tse-tan asked how soon it would be over, he shook his close-cropped head. 'The Japanese say it has never begun. For us it is a war of resistance. We can only resist and resist, never thinking about any ending. Even if we never win a battle, as long as we continue to resist, Japan can never win either.'

For Yü this interminable struggle was something from from which he shrank. 'That is too long a time.'

'What matter the length? We have millions and millions of men. Japan cannot kill in a day as many as are born; so if we do not give in we must finally succeed.' It was as clear as that to Colonel Wu.

The Artist shook his head. 'Too long. Too long.' He repeated the words. 'It is not you important military gentlemen, nor the noisy patriotic students, like those here at Jen Dah, who are fighting the war. It is the farmers, and the farmers' sons. The sons of the poeple of Wheelbarrow Lane who are being forced into the army. Are they willing to fight on and on without any end?'

'We must keep a united determination to resist until victory comes,' agreed Wu. 'Our danger is lest the communist-bandits betray us,' – he still used the old term despite the alliance reached after the Sian kidnapping. 'But there can be no quick ending without foreign aid.' He turned to me. 'This is not only China's war, it is the war of all democratic nations against aggression. We are fighting for your country, and yours,' he included Molly by a wave of his hand. 'When you pray ask your God that England and America may soon come to help us.'

Colonel Wu was scornful of the peaceful atmosphere of Duliang. 'You live in a well, all you people here. You look only at a narrow circle of sky, and know nothing about what is going on down-river, not even at Chungking; you know nothing of the war. You, here in the *heo-fang,* behind the lines, live as though the world was going on as usual, you go on teaching school as if nothing were happening.'

Then he softened, and said to me: 'Perhaps it is a good thing to teach. Go on with it, keep the students busy and quiet, no running off to join the communists at Yenan. Keep them working and let us get on with the war.'

At Jen Dah, among our student body, now larger than ever before, there was no rush to join the army; the pressure indeed was all in the other direction. Many saw themselves as being trained to build up the country after the war. Even though the old saying, that good iron was not used for making nails and good men were not for making soldiers, was replaced by an often repeated slogan: 'Good sons be-come soldiers and kill the enemy,' very few students seemed to believe it applied to them. Perhaps, as Colonel Wu said, our job was to keep them busy at their studies. Indeed a govern-ment directive had been received advising that we could best serve the country by carrying on as far as possible as if condi-tions were normal, avoiding war psychology, giving our own students and our refugee guests the opportunity to finish their training, actual fighting being left to the soldiers.

'Our military equipment may not be as good as that of Japan, but we shall win our war of resistance through the operation of economic forces and the indomitable spirit of our awakened people.' Colonel Wu's final words sounded as if they were the peroration to a familiar lecture delivered to his staff. As Molly and I left, the two men turned again to their birds.

From what Molly told me it appeared that Deh-min had been a little anxious lest his father might blame him because they had not treated Old Mother in a more lavish manner. But the Colonel was pleased. 'It is good to live simply,' he told them. 'Our Generalissimo rightly stresses this as part of the New Life Movement. We cannot win the war unless we use all our energy and give all our money to resist Japan.' He was advising Second Son, Deh-liang, in Shanghai to sell their mansion there, if he could find a buyer, and live in a simpler, small house they owned. Although both French Concession and International Settlement were secure at the moment, no one could foretell what the future might bring. If the sale were accomplished, the money, Molly believed, would not go to resist Japan but, if there was still time, to an account in America which was being built up as the final security for the family.

As I walked back up the Lane, I looked at the posters on the walls, and at a great canvas slung on ropes across the street. They seemed bloodier than ever: death, torture, agony, rape in all its nakedness, every picture designed to arouse the passions and the will of the people to resist. 'Resist': this was the key word, on everyone's lips, on every poster. China certainly was not fighting a war of aggression or expansion. She was resisting a deadly onslaught, determined to fight and never give in. There was a new poster in flaming colours: a Japanese soldier cutting off the breasts of a Chinese girl. Gruesome, not to be forgotten, but so like the familiar scenes in the old Buddhist temples which for generations have encouraged or warned the Chinese people. The delights of the blessed, the torments of the damned, all depicted in life-size figures. Devils torturing plaster wrong-doers in every conceivable manner: naked women impaled on wooden stakes, others sliced or burned, nails being torn by the fiends from toes and fingers, breasts cut by ugly knives, limbs broken. Could the modern posters, so much in the ancient tradition, affect the people of the Lane as much as they haunted me?

Down the road, coming towards me, was a group of our Jen Dah students going to a mass-meeting to strengthen the will of the people to resist Japan. They carried flags and gay-coloured banners, on which were slogans in black and red. With them were boy scouts from Jen Hsiao, the smaller ones running to keep up with the rest. All wore khaki shirts of various shades and had puttees and shorts. There were also girl guides, with bright shining faces, all dressed in ugly black skirts of thin silk or cotton. They too wore khaki shirts, but also black stockings and small peaked hats on their heads. Their necks were smothered in their black ties. One and all had eyes that sparkled; and their eager enthusiasm proclaimed them as the ardent young workers of the *heo-fang* of China. Lustily, though not much in unison, they sang as they marched:

Arise, Arise,
With our heart's blood we will build a new Wall of China.
Labourers and farmers, soldiers and students,
Let us unite to save our home-land!
Leave office and fields; leave shops and classrooms.
Away to the front with the army of freedom.
March on, on, on.*

*In September, 1949, this stirring march of resistance was adopted, after some slight changes in the words, as the national anthem of the People's Republic of China.

IX

Napoleon Departs

AFTER THE JAPANESE had captured Hankow and its neighbouring cities in October 1938, air raids on West China
commenced. They were directed primarily against Chungking, but also against the provincial capital, Chengtu.
Sometimes, on the way to or from the latter, the Japanese
planes passed over Duliang. The great distance they had
come, and the excellent warning system the Chinese
managed to maintain, meant that there was ample time in
which to prepare. A first alarm, accompanied by waving
yellow flags indicated that the planes had left Hankow,
heading west towards Ichang. The second, some hours later,
with red flags, meant that they had passed Chungking; and
about twenty minutes after that the black flag urgently
warned that they were upon us. Most frequently the first
alarm was followed by the all clear, the planes returning east
after raiding the national capital.

When the alarm sounded, Duliang evacuated itself. The
people hurriedly made for the four gates in the city walls,
one at each point of the compass: East, South, West and
North. Each person took with him his most valued possessions. Small children, and aged parents or ailing relatives had
to be carried if they were unable to walk or, being too poor,
no rickshaws had been secured for them. Shopkeepers made
little wooden carts, which were hastily laden with their
stock in trade. The pressure at the gates was enormous,

rickshaws, bicycles, carts, jammed in the compact mass of people, wedged tightly together, forced through the opening, the young and agile often walking on the shoulders of the solid mass. The few who stumbled, and were not carried forward in the crowd, were trodden to pulp underfoot. It was so terrible that the people demanded that the great gates themselves be pulled down and gaps enlarged in the high walls. It was then easier to escape; but always there was danger from the mindless horde, driven by frightening pressure to pass through the openings. Once out of the city the people made for the open country, learning by bitter experience that they must lie hidden in the beans and rape or rice, according to the season, for there was no anti-aircraft fire to discourage the raiders from flying low and machine-gunning those who were seen on the narrow country paths or village streets.

Deh-min had arranged with a workman on the Lane to come at first alarm with a wheelbarrow for Old Mother. It was considered safer to be away from the city rather than trusting his dugout shelter. He himself bicycled along the country paths from the Leather College and arrived in time to join his fleeing family: Old Mother cushioned from the jolts of the wheelbarrow by a padded quilt, Deh-chin and Molly carrying baskets of food, Lai-ma with Mei-mei in a basket on her back. Go-go and Di-di were spurred on by the others, occasionally carried on their father's shoulders. They made their way among the stream of anxious people to a farm about a mile away where Deh-min had rented a room, which he had protected by sand-bags against stray bullets.

Terrible stories of the raids upon Chungking were told in the tea-shop on the Lane, but despite the machine-gunning no bombs had been dropped on Duliang. It appeared to be the Japanese policy to demoralise the people by disorganizing their lives. This in some measure they accomplished, as time and time again so many from the city trailed into the country. In fact when people were beginning to grow careless and stay at home the Japanese dropped leaflets: 'Save up your money to buy shoes. We shall continue coming, and you will have to keep walking to the country places.'

How we grew to hate the beautiful sunny days, for it was out of the cloudless skies that the planes would come to our distant province. 'Let us hope the dull mist will continue all day,' was the first thought when, on rising, people found the city covered by an autumnal fog. During the winter, cloudy Szechwan had a natural protection, enabling people to lead more normal lives. Yet at any time there was the possibility of alarms. No one knew when they might have to lay down their work, stop their teaching or business, and go out to the fields. During fine weather our time-table at Jen Dah was altered so that classes were at dawn and late afternoon, leaving the middle of the day free for whatever might happen. Even the children could think of no games to play except *deo fei-dji*, hiding from planes. Go-go and Di-di, playing with their friends, in this way released some of the tensions caused by the all too real and infectious fear of the adults.

Usually after an alarm I remained in the Science Building at Jen Dah. Its brick walls were adequate against bullets, and it seemed unlikely that the Japanese would deliberately bomb a foreign institution. When planes did fly overhead there was a deadly hush. Those students, remaining with me in the laboratory, believed, as did everyone else, that the Japanese had means of hearing even whispered conversations, so that any talk was likely to attract attention. Sometimes after a yellow warning I went out to the farm to picnic with Molly and Deh-min. One occasion was a few days after the news had come that the Second World War had started in Europe. It was a glorious sunny day, and the paths, though thronged, were less crowded than in the earlier days. The tradesmen with their little hand carts were there, for they knew that if a raid took place there would be no compensation for any loss. The children, some carried in baskets, had come to regard these excursions as a holiday. The sick and the aged were now often left at home. It was no longer a common sight to see them being carried in the arms or on the shoulders of strong, filial sons. People were tending to stay at home until the red flag alarm, then hurrying to the nearby fields.

This time I met a group of doctors and nurses from our hospital and, in crude unthinking western manner, teasingly asked them if they had deserted their patients. They were all in dark clothes, their usual white coats and aprons left behind. It was forbidden to wear white after an alarm, fearing lest the raiders should be attracted. Only suspected spies left their

white washing spread upon the ground, or hanging from bamboo poles to dry.

My doctor friends were hurt and idignant. 'There are so few of us. What would happen to the patients if we or the nurses lost our lives? If there were a raid, what would the victims do if we were dead? The people depend upon us.'

I was reminded of Mrs Bao. At the very first alarm her husband, Bao Hsin-min, sometimes alone, sometimes with the older children, went quickly to the country, while she was left to take care of the post office. 'Of course he must go,' she explained. 'He earns the money. If anything happened to him, what could we do without him? We make him go at once.'

As a result of this excursion to the farm, Molly and Deh-chin came to have supper with me, Deh-min agreeing to stay at home to look after Old Mother. The occasion was not a success. The news of war in Europe had made me anxious about my family, and Molly about her mother. I was also conscious that I had been insensitive, failing in tact, when teasing my medical colleagues that morning. I valued their friendship, realized their worth, and their devotion.

Also it happened that Fu Lu-chin was ill. Molly went to see him in his little room where he was in bed, a white cloth wound round his temples. His wife cooked the meal, which she did only moderately well, Cook Fu shouting instructions to her through the open kitchen window.

Fu had told Molly that there had been a row that morning. '*La-ge nü*, that girl', who it turned out was Sylvia, had been out to play tennis once again with 'that student'. She and Napoleon still came occasionally, soon after daybreak, so that their games could be finished before there was danger of any alarm. That morning they had come later than usual, and the alarm had been earlier. The girl had not been able to return to the city. Despite the hole in the wall, no rickshaw, no person, could possibly make any headway against the torrent pouring out. Sylvia had been hysterical. She must get back. They – whoever *they* were – would kill her, she said. 'Bad business, bad business,' Fu summed it up to Molly. We were anxious about them. I knew remarkably little, not even Sylvia's Chinese name, and Molly could add only that Napoleon had been to her home when the Colonel was there. Nap had been introduced to her as the son of a fellow officer now in Chungking.

A further cloud was cast by a letter, delivered by the postman shortly after the all clear had been sounded. It was from the banker, Hsiung Wei-lin. There had been some sadness after their marriage, as Ruby had a miscarriage. Then to their delight a son was born. They had written to tell of their joy, which had now all departed as this new letter disclosed. 'My baby is dead. I do not know what is wrong. During these two months I lost my mother and now my son. How bad this is. Nobody is unfortunate like me in the world. I think Heaven hates me; but what have I done?' Molly and I were upset by this sorrow which had come to these two friends or ours. Although, typically, Hsiung made no mention of Ruby, we could imagine the grief she must be feeling.

While Molly and I were talking, Deh-chin said nothing. She was wearing a simple blue jacket over a pale yellow gown. Her heavy hair, now grown longer, hung down over her shoulders in two plaits, each tied with a ribbon, also yellow to match her gown. She had been sitting quietly ever since we had finished the meal. Suddenly, unexpectedly, there came an emotional outburst, obviously long suppressed. The words poured out: 'This baby of the Hsiungs. One dead baby. What of it? What of its parents grief? There are untold dead babies – so many, they are without number. They die like the flies you swat, in every city, in every village. Their parents know it is useless to plan or to dream. They must not grieve, for life is nothing but grief. They cannot question

Heaven, for they live always under its curse. They must accept life with its cruelty, its hardness – for they have no hope of ever altering their lot. You two, you foreigners, what can you know? You have never had a chance of knowing. Deh-min couldn't tell you, Molly, for he too never sees anything. His eyes are not open. If you are rich you are safe; you can buy everything you need, not just food but security, justice, privilege. If you are poor, you have only bitterness and sorrow to eat.'

The words came as a torrent, not shouted, almost hissed as a whisper, but driven by an intense power behind them, like the mass of humanity discharged through the city gate after an alarm. 'You talk about Wheelbarrow Lane and the people there – but what do you know about them? When you look you see fantasy. It is beautiful, romantic; even the odd is attractive to you. You can escape – but they escape never.' She repeated that word of a lasting doom: never. 'The Lane, it is so picturesque – but that is just for you who look on. For them it is foul. They fight each other in order to live. They defraud, they deceive. They sell themselves for a few grains of rice – they have to in order to keep alive. And the next moment they have to sell themselves again, and then again. They can have no self-respect. They have no hope. They are caught in a trap.'

Molly and I sat there saying nothing, too embarrassed to look at each other. After the first outburst, Deh-chin was speaking more softly. 'Over the country, this city, this Lane of ours, there hangs a perpetual cloud. No one knows when disaster may strike. I do not mean Japanese bombs or bullets, but death-blows from our own Chinese people. When a man goes out he finds on his return that his home has been pillaged by hungry disorganized soldiers, his family taken for ransom, his children not seen again. Unjust taxation robs him of all his savings – driving him into the terrifying hands of the money-lender. No security, no justice – the law is not for those without money. Now there is conscription, but just for the poor – not for those who can pay, or have friends with influence. And those who are taken never come back.'

It was Molly who recovered first, and interrupted to say: 'This may in some measure be true, but it is only part of the picture. Who gave you all these ideas?' As she looked at her sister-in-law's earnest face, she decided that after all Deh-chin was not like her brother. Molly had never seen that look of intense dedication in her husband's eyes. Deh-chin was transformed: no longer the innocent, sweet girl she had believed her to be.

'In Shanghai I had a friend. He knew everything: his eyes were open. He took me to places and I saw for myself. I saw how rich people, like those who came to our house, made it impossible for the poor to live happily, took the heart out of them, denied education to their children, used their strength in the factories and then, when they were worn out, diseased and useless, turned them adrift. I saw it for myself.'

Suddenly she must have become aware of the way she was speaking. 'Promise, please promise, you will not tell the others what I have said' – and Molly and I, still under her spell, gave her our promise. Molly, I could see, was shaken. This was strange talk she was hearing from the pampered daughter of an important official, brought up in one of the more wealthy homes of Shanghai.

Deh-chin had not yet finished. She turned to me: 'Your eyes too are closed, like Deh-min's. You think it is all quiet among your students; but really it is all bubbling and boiling underneath. They want to do something for their country, to act, to fight. But the government is afraid of them because they are honest and have many ideas. It insists that they study. It tells them that China wants future leaders, but that is all an excuse. You are ordered to keep them out of mischief; but they ought to be using their energy and their knowledge now to defeat Japan. Mao Tse-tung who is

fighting the Japanese in the north knows better. He understands the restless urge in the hearts of young men and
women. At Yenan he trains men to fight, and women to
strengthen the resistance of the people. He says: "We are
like fleas, biting the Japanese and preventing them having any
peace and quiet." '

Deh-chin shattered the naive simplicity of our picture
of a brave China at war. 'Beat Japan and help the people' was
her purpose, and the purpose of youth, she told us. We were
realizing that what she had said had put her safety, perhaps
her life, into our hands. 'And remember, Molly, it is not
only Old Mother, but Deh-min who must not know.
Although the time may soon come when you can tell them.'
It was with some distaste that Molly realized she had promised
to keep a secret from her husband.

Deh-chin told more about the young man in Shanghai.
'We have pledged with our blood. Even now I am preparing.
I read when Old Mother is asleep. When the time comes, I
shall be ready.' During the visit of Colonel Wu she had
heard her parents discussing her in Old Mother's bedroom.
'They tried once before, but if they are again planning to
marry me to someone of their choice I shall not give them
the chance. I shall go north to the Resist-Japan University at
Yenan, and leave them.' Then looking at Molly she added:
'Somehow I don't think they will at present. They wouldn't
really trust you to look after Old Mother. So you are really
my salvation.' The affectionate squeeze she gave Molly's
hand softened the blow she had so thoughtlessly dealt.
Molly was crushed to think she was not entirely accepted.

★

The start of the Second World War made life more
difficult in Wheelbarrow Lane, although there was now hope
that eventually China would not have to struggle alone
against the invader. The Yangste had already been closed to

shipping, but now the British yielded to Japanese pressure and closed the Burma Road to most traffic, so that fewer goods came to the west of China. The air link between Chungking and Hong Kong was operated only at night. The cost of living was steadily rising, and for teachers and government employees life was far from easy. Deh-min was earning less than many coolies in Duliang, and at the same time was under pressure to help establish more factories for the production of leather.

There were great difficulties in the Chemistry Department at Jen Dah. We were driven to depend on local supplies, altering many of the experiments the students performed. We developed new skills and new techniques. We collected and sorted broken glass, and from it our technicians soon learnt skilfully to blow fresh apparatus. Down-river guest students were wasteful in their habits, and even in normal times would have been difficult to manage, for even then all our supplies had to be ordered a full year in advance, with no shops round the corner in case of urgent need.

When we were almost desperate, a consignment of student balances arrived from England. They had been more than two years on the way, and must have come through the Japanese lines. We unpacked the cases one afternoon, while students were doing practical work. There had been no raid that day, so classes were normal.

Near the Science Building was a small, shallow lake, fed from an irrigation ditch, and fringed with tall graceful willows. It was not only beautiful but useful: a hunting ground for the biologists who found there many of the specimens they needed. That afternoon the Biology coolie, Lao Bei, was out with his net.

I was talking to a couple of students about the experiment they were doing together, making some suggestions about improving their apparatus, when I was aware that Lao Bei was standing behind me. 'Look, Hsien-sen,' he said. I turned.

In his net was a human foot. After all these years I can still feel the shock that moment gave me.

He had brought it to me, I supposed, rather than taking it to the Biology Department upstairs, because I was a foreigner. Prestige was involved, and I had to suppress the nausea I felt. 'Put it on the waterproof paper,' was all I could say, pointing to the corner where we had been unpacking the balances, and where Lao Du, our own coolie, was carefully collecting the paper.

A few minutes later, Lao Bei was back again with another piece of body – bloodless, flaccid, washed to an inhuman whiteness. Piece by piece the horror grew – a jig-saw on the laboratory floor.

The Jen Dah private police were called. They opened the wide sluice gates of the lake to empty it. The head was found and placed where it belonged. It was no one we could recognize: the cheeks had been sliced and the front teeth knocked out.

This obscene thing was accepted by the students with a calmness I could not share, and certainly did not attempt to equal. On open days when the public flocked to look over Jen Dah, one of the most sought-after exhibits was the pickled human male in our Anatomy Department. He had been completely divided into many sections, all arranged in order in their neat glass containers. There were scores of these pieces, but on the floor there were little more than a dozen, which Lao Du, together with Lao Bei, had fitted together.

'Frightening,' said one girl as she leaned over the bench to see what was lying on the floor. 'Terrifying,' echoed her companion. Then after a few moments they returned to their experiment.

Our technician, Sung, was a reader of detective stories. The open, mutilated mouth must have given him an idea. He had cycled to the Dental Department and brought back with him two of the surgeons. Sung had observed that the back teeth were filled. Nowhere else in Duliang, except in our hospital, was this likely to have been done. The identification took a little time for the fillings had not been done at Jen Dah, but had been noted in a recent patient. There was no doubt about it. The pieces had once been Napoleon Chen.

One vital part was missing. The police were still searching in the lake. My senior student, Chen Deh-li, who was assisting with the class, shook his head. They will never find it.' He was very definite.

When I looked at him enquiringly he spoke a single word in English: 'Mincemeat.'

It was so revolting that I could only laugh with half-hysterical relaxation of the tension I was feeling. The whole affair became entirely unreal. The pale pieces were no longer Nap, the young man I had known. They were merely specimens, unpleasant, but without emotional associations.

'It is a way we have in our part of China,' Chen Deh-li was telling me. 'Mutilation . . .'

'Horrible mutilation,' broke in Technician Sung, who was standing by his side, also anxious to make the situation clear to me.

'Mutilation, in which those parts which have offended most are singled out for special punishment.'

'So we know what he was punished for,' Sung was determined I should understand.

'Please call the police, the real police, the city police,' I ordered. But both Sung and Chen Deh-li stood where they were and laughed.

'Useless,' Sung said. 'Didn't you know that the girl who used to play tennis on your court was the pet concubine of the Chief of Police? It is he who must have had this done. The missing part shows the reason – but although it is plain, you could never prove it. Never!'

We looked out of the window at our police, who were responsible for order on the Campus. The emptying lake was already getting quite shallow. They were gathering up fish. 'Tonight they will be selling them on Wheelbarrow Lane. They have already forgotten our friend here. They will make money.' Chen smiled at me.

So all that could be gathered together of Napoleon Chen, wrapped in the waterproof paper, was placed in one of the boxes recently arrived from England. As Lao Du nailed down the lid, the stencilled name of the firm from whom the balances had come, *George & Becker* of *Hatton Wall*, utterly denied the nature of the contents. The two coolies carried the box downstairs to the basement and left it locked up in an outhouse.

Napoleon's relative in Duliang was traced. To my surprise the situation was accepted and no attempt made to track down those who so expertly had carried out the execution. He probably knew more than I did, and realized the futility of any complaint.

The last we saw was the relative and his servant leaving the campus in two street rickshaws, followed by a third to which the box had awkwardly been tied.

What happened to Sylvia I cannot tell. She was never seen again by anyone I knew. Life must have been made hard for her. It is even possible she may have shared Nap's fate.

A few weeks later in Wheelbarrow Lane, I was attracted by a sign at the butcher's shop. It announced in bold characters that he was selling pork at one thousand two hundred cash a catty. The unsuspecting shopper, drawn by the low price, would discover that actually in finer writing it said one thousand five hundred and ninety-nine. I was feeling rather pleased with myself for having noticed this rather ridiculous trick, when Molly's sister-in-law, who was passing, stopped to ask if I was buying meat. I made some frivolous reply about the butcher's sign; but she was not amused.

Deh-chin, with a new familiarity since she knew I was aware of her own dedication, admonished me, yet kindly. 'It is true your eyes are not fully opened.' This blindness of others obsessed her. 'You are too romantic to see the reality below the surface. Do you think men like to gain their livelihood by deceiving others? The butcher is compelled to do this because of the rotten society in which we live. Someday the time will come when all men can live honest lives, and deception of any kind will no longer be necessary.'

As she left me, she turned and added. 'You may be interested to know that I shall not have to go north after all – at least not at present. The man cut up and put into your lake was the one his father and mine were planning I should marry.'

X

Little Boy Bao

<hr>

IT WAS MRS FU who told me the news as she brought me my breakfast. Her husband, hovering between brown and white turbans, those signs of the state of his health, usually got up later, and left her to prepare food. As she gave me my bacon and eggs, she said, in a matter of fact way as though it was the commonest thing in the world to have happened: 'The Bao little boy has gone.'

It took me some time to realize just what she meant. The Bao's child had vanished two days previously and could not be found.

An hour or two later, after a lecture which I had to give, I was able to visit the post office. As I walked from the Science Building, I passed the small bed already prepared for scattering the rice seed, which when grown into seedlings would be transplanted in the flooded fields. The air was decidedly warmer, and there was that morning the glad promise of sunshine. The early days of spring had arrived. I had a feeling of buoyancy, which was not entirely dispelled when I heard the first or yellow air-raid alarm. During the winter with its clouds we had been free for many weeks from all raids. It was hard to believe they were starting again.

Bao Hsin-min was out in the Lane, bargaining for a rickshaw – one of the decrepit kind which their owners were willing to risk on the rough country roads leading to other towns. On the post office step Mrs Bao was sitting, head buried in hands, her quiet sobbing broken every few moments by a heart-rending wail. When he saw me, Hsin-min's tired face broke into a smile. Yes, his boy had not returned home – but it was of no great importance.

When I asked him which son, for I knew he had several, he told me that it was the eleven-year-old.

'Not the killer of flies?' My dismay was increasing. After meeting the child at the banker's wedding, he had always bowed his head with a word of greeting whenever he saw me.

'Just that one.' Bao's smile reappeared – very obviously forced; and he laughed aloud. The sound was unbearable for I knew that he, like his wife, was in deepest distress. It was disconcerting to be confronted by this polite stoic determination to prevent me being embarrassed by their personal grief. Many Chinese friends will tell of the death of parent or spouse, or much beloved child, with smiles on their faces. But although faces wear smiles, it is said, hearts often beat heavy.

My questions were torturing Bao. If I was to get more information or help him, I knew I must ask someone else and save him the distress of this personal encounter. As on so many other occasions when I needed help, information or comfort, I set off down the Lane to see my old teacher, Yü Tse-tan.

His servant led me to the inner courtyard where Yü came to the door of his studio in welcome. 'A bad business,' he agreed, when I told him why I had come. 'Not good, not good at all. After school his mother sent him to buy soy-bean sauce. He was not seen again.'

'But how can that be?' I could not believe that a child could be lost in the Lane. 'The family is well known – everyone goes to the post office. Someone must have seen him.'

The artist wiped his watering eyes and gave a short apologetic laugh. 'But no one did see him. The last person was one of the men at Carpenter Deng's who saw him come out of the post office, dangling the empty bottle on a string. He was swinging it, the way boys do, as he went down the Lane.'

'But at the soy shop?'

'He never got there. Of course they have many customers, but they all know young Bao.' Yü spoke about the parents' grief. They had gone from door to door, notices were put up in the tea-shop, but no one could help.

There were many possibilities. Most hopeful was that he might have been taken by boatmen to serve as extra crew or to cook the food. Then they might sell him to some other boat, perhaps in Chungking, so that in time news would get back to his home. The boy was attractive: he might have been stolen by some childless family who wanted a son. If he had been a girl, there were brothels which could have been searched; and there were still some large mansions in which, although forbidden, they kept little girls as slaves.

I wondered if he might have gone to play near the river and been drowned, but Yü shook his head. 'Most unlikely.' Then the artist became confidential. 'Last night Bao had a letter from someone, who knew someone, who had got information that the child was being held for ransom. They could not tell if the letter were true or false – it was all very vague. If Bao had been wealthy the boy might have been kidnapped, but he was poor. Yet times are hard, and a postal official has more money than most of us.'

When I had seen him that morning, Bao Hsin-min was setting off to sell some land he owned. Like most people he purchased fields with any money he saved. It seemed risky to me: 'He may lose all his money if it turns out to be all a trick.'

Yü Tse-tan accepted the possibility and showed none of the anxiety which I was feeling on Bao's behalf. 'They like the boy. What else could they do?' So carefully to count material costs may be a western trait.

'What chance is there of getting him back?' The question was blunt. I should never have asked it of Bao himself.

'Very little. Perhaps they will never know anything more. Usually when children vanish that is the end of it.' Only afterwards did I realize no one had mentioned reporting the missing boy to the police and seeking their help – a reflection on the administration of law and order in Duliang at that time.

We sat quietly, without talking, until the well-loved room calmed me. When I arrived Yü had been writing some large characters on a sheet of white paper spread out before him. He now started to grind fresh ink. He held back his voluminous sleeve as he rubbed the black stick on the smooth slab with a circular motion, pausing now and then to add a few drops of water from a tall china tea pot, with a broken spout. It was soothing to watch him as he went on and on – so many of the actions of old Chinese scholars seemed designed to bring an unhurried calmness to life. As I glanced round the room I realized how familiar it had become since the first time he entertained us, when with Molly and Deh-min we had met Hsiung and Bao. In part of the room was the artist's clutter, his bundles of scrolls, his papers and brushes. There was a cupboard with a large brass butterfly clasp and a long brass lock. In winter, in the middle of the room, there was always a large iron brazier in a wide wooden frame. It was pleasant to sit round it, feet on the broad edges, and with the long iron tongs move the brightly glowing charcoal from place to place. It was a room of peace and repose. Even the noise from the courtyard, the shouting of servants, the distant clack-clack of the loom, and Mrs Yü rattling the bowls as she stumped in on her tiny bound feet to offer tea, all blended to give an aura of calm.

In the past the room had possessed little comfort. The few chairs, although beautifully carved and with marble seats and backs, were stiff and upright, four square, placed against one of the walls in pairs, with a table for tea bowls between them. The only concession to human weakness was a low bamboo chair, little more than a stool, which yielded slightly to the body, and had a sloping back against which to relax. But now, a sign of the times, there was a new arm chair, with padded cushion seat, made by Carpenter Deng from a pattern one of the refugees had brought from the coast.

The familiar scrolls were still hanging on the walls, but from the easy chair, which Yü had insisted I should try, I saw one which was new to me. Tse-tan told me that he had painted it after the loss of Nanking to the Japanese. Through enveloping dark clouds a lake could be seen, surrounded by bending willows, beaten down by relentless driving rain. In it was the anguish that the Chinese people felt at the occupation of their historic city, which was followed by such cruel rape and murder. Yet the picture, one knew, was not entire despair – the stricken trees were rooted in the earth and would live, in their leaves there was still the green of life. Typhoons do not blow for ever; and after the rain comes the sunshine.

I asked him about his little sketches of the people of the Lane; but inspiration had left him. There were no people in his scroll of Nanking, and he showed me one or two ink drawings of strange shaped rocks, with bamboos growing from them, of twisted branches, patched with lichens. Nature had become his refuge. He had turned from the world of evil men to the great universe itself, to Heaven, which absorbed him for he was part of it. While wrong was rampant he ignored the transient for the eternal. People were unprincipled and cruel to each other, to their children, but virtue remained in things themselves. *(see page 105).*

When I emerged into the bustling Lane through the weaver's shed, Old Wu Tai-tai was sitting in her chair at the end of the alley by Tailor Su's shop. She had taken advantage of the sunshine. The seller of dog-skin plasters, shoving his

quaint cart, had stopped to talk to her. He was still wearing his winter wind-hood and padded cape, but if he had been questioned would almost certainly have pointed to one of the tung-oil trees which grew at the edge of Hercules Park. They were in bud, but not yet in flower, and 'beggars must still be wary, and not shed their winter clothes, until the blossoms come out.'

He was telling the merits of his plasters, so efficient when placed on boils or pimples, cuts or even festering sores. Old Mother herself was interested in medicines and glad to talk. On fine days, Deh-chin would often go with her out through the little gate at the back to the grassy graveland, seeking medicines for children's ailments, hibiscus for eyes, and trefoil useful in cooking. Memories of girlhood experience came back to old Mrs Wu. She would go to the kitchen to see that the plants she gathered were prepared as tradition demanded.

Old Mother, as Molly told me, seemed quite at peace, although the Lane itself seethed with its restless life. The landlord's old house, with its heavenly wells, reminded her of the days before she had been married and taken to live in a Shanghai mansion. Occasionally she expressed very definite views about the upbringing of her grandchildren, but never complained at the inconveniences she must have felt. It was as though she had slipped away from the exotic life of Shanghai, back into rural China. She accepted the lack of electric light, the open cesspool instead of covered drains, the absence of piped water. It remained her great enjoyment, when Deh-chin took her bamboo chair out to the Lane, to sit watching the people, talking to the many she had come to know.

Molly was anxious that morning because of the loss of Fly-killing Bao. She could hardly bear her children to be out of her sight. Mei-mei, now three, never went beyond Landlord Lee's gate by herself; and Molly insisted that Go-go and Di-di should never go singly to or from school. 'I dare not try to imagine how Mrs Bao must be feeling,' she was saying, when there was a sudden wild commotion: cries of terror and warning which came from all round us. This time it was no individual tragedy, but a dread which touched us all. In a moment, the vibrant scream of planes flying so low that the room, its furniture and the house itself shook. Falling bombs screeched, and in the deafening crash of explosions the whole earth was rocking.

We had forgotten the yellow warning, given so early that morning. We had heard no further alarm; indeed it is doubtful if any was given. The planes had come by an unusual route direct to Duliang, instead of first dropping their bombs on Chungking or Chengtu. Many times we had been

machine-gunned, but this was the first occasion our city
was bombed.

Again came the drone of planes, falling bombs screamed,
and again the earth shook as they burst – but Molly and I were
running down the alley to rescue Old Mother. Deh-chin was
already with her. The two women hurried her back through
the courtyards to take her to the shelter – but already the
planes had gone back to the east.

After the explosions there was silence: not a bird chirped.
Then came a roar of voices, angry and frightened. It grew
until it seemed that every man, woman and child was
crying to Heaven. Before the sound dwindled to a low
murmur, Deh-min arrived back from his college. For him,
also, there had been no red alarm, but he had heard a final
warning. As black flags waved he hurried home, anxious for
his mother. He expected to find her wrapped in warm rugs,
safe in the dugout.

'If the bombs had been nearer, Old Mother might have
been killed or injured.' He was angry because of the risk they
had taken.

'They didn't, however, and she and the rest of us are alive
and unharmed. We had no time to shelter.' Molly was calm.
Deh-min rarely sought a quarrel.

'Cannot I be away even for a short time,' he was angrily
saying, when Old Mother broke in.

'*Swan-lo, swan-lo.* Stop talking nonsense. When there is no
man about the house, women are too busy to spend time
popping people into holes as though they were toads or
rabbits.'

A great cloud of dust rose billowing from within the city
walls. As it soared it spread, darkening the earth as the sun
was obscured. When I got to the city to give what help I
could, victims were still being dragged from the rubble and
matchwood. Those who were dead were placed wherever
flat ground remained, while doctors and nurses were

kneeling by those who still lived. Relatives were gathering in groups, burning their incense, prostrating themselves. There was weeping and crying aloud, and hurried consultations about what should be done. Those who lived in an age that for most of the world has long since departed, had been suddenly invaded by the twentieth century with its stark selfish cruelty, its technical efficiency at its most evil; they had been overtaken by world events of which they knew little. They were entirely defenceless in an old Asian city from which not a shot had been fired; the victims of raiders, who were free to come and go as they wished.

After leaving the bombed area I took a rickshaw back to Jen Dah. When I was paying him, the puller, thin and old, unfit for the work he was doing, scratched his turbaned head and asked: 'You foreign people are fighting us Chinese. Tell me, Hsien-sen, who is winning? Are you or are we?' There was no personal hatred, no condemnation. He had no feeling that the war was in any way his. It was a simple request for information about a conflict in which he was unwillingly involved.

A few days later I had to pass through the bombed part of the city. Already 'homes' were being made from the wreckage. On a board or two, people were offering for sale small useful articles and fragments saved from the ruins. In places there lingered the faint sickly smell of decomposition; but on top of a heap of wood and broken tiles a woman was sitting. She was selling twigs of prunus flowers, which she had arranged all around her. The blaze of pink, red and white blossoms made the heart leap: here was a beauty which even the Japanese bombs could not destroy.

The sight of the ruins was emotionally disturbing and on my way home I decided again to visit the artist who was always so calm. He too was evidently troubled. He was sitting listless in his new chair, neither smoking nor apparently with any urge to work. The characters which he was writing on the day of the raid were still unfinished, the paper lying undisturbed on the table. He rose to offer me his chair but I stood looking at what he had written. 'Yes,' he said, *'China's Year of Victory.* It is a good slogan to enhearten the people. Our leader, the Generalissimo, tells us that we must strive to make it come true. But tell me,' and taking off his glasses he leaned forward until his face was close to mine, 'do you see victory coming this year? In July we enter the fifth year of the war, and all this time China has been fighting alone. It is wonderful that we are undefeated, a tribute to our soldiers and our leaders, but I see no end unless other nations join us in the struggle against powerful Japan.'

He was pleased when I told him that it was believed that war in Europe must inevitably spread to the Pacific. 'Then America will send her aeroplanes to help us, and the Japanese when they come to bomb will meet with resistance.' It is true that China had a handful of planes, but they were mostly for training, and at first alarm they flew westward lest they were destroyed on the ground.

He was troubled, I discovered, not only by the bombing of the city, but also because of the tragedy of his friend Bao Hsin-min. The story he told me about the loss of the boy was so complex that I never was sure I understood it completely. Bao sold his fields, but could not raise sufficient to pay all the ransom demanded. He had written to the kidnappers through an intermediary – a polite letter to thank them for looking after the boy, but pointing out that poverty made it impossible for him to pay what they asked 'for his board and lodging'. At great expense he entertained the powerful leaders of the secret *Ko Lao* Society, hoping they might intercede on his behalf. The price, indeed, was said to have been reduced by half. Although the money was paid, the boy was not returned. 'That is the way things are,' Yü concluded with resignation, mopping his eyes, as we remained silent. His face, which I was watching, suddenly lit up. His own son, Yü

Go-go, had come from the Middle School, where he was now a student. Although no word was spoken, I knew that the artist's pride in the boy was tinged with fear.

To Bao Hsin-min himself I did not again mention his loss, yet whenever I saw him I felt pity as I remembered his son, who killed so many flies and in whom his parents had such high hopes. For the first few days after he was lost, Mrs Bao sat on the post office step, quietly crying, looking up and down the Lane, still hoping to see the boy break from the crowd and come towards her. Yet the very interest she had in others, which made her the Lane's matchmaker, meant that her thoughts could not for long dwell on her own sorrow. I saw one of her children toddle towards her. She reached out towards him and sat him on her knees, pressing her cheek against the child's. *Swan-lo,* it is finished. I knew that for her life would go on once more.

It was impossible for any of us to dwell on the risks to which we were exposed: there was far too much to be done. In Jen Dah the pressure from dealing with the refugee students, who flocked to us from the coastal provinces, was really enormous, especially as the shortage of books and scientific equipment was daily growing greater. We tried to forget our personal cares, but we who were British were anxious because of the war in Europe; and those from the United States wondered what the worsening relations between their country and Japan might mean. We all of us shared with our Chinese colleagues the strain of the war, which was specially felt by our refugee guests, many of whom had no news of their families, or the homes they had left.

In Wheelbarrow Lane there was a growing unease. It was not only that the air-raid alarms were disturbing, but the new-comers, who now thronged the streets, brought fresh ideas with them. Local people came to feel that they were behind the times, in some ways inferior, and in consequence they were often aggressive. In the tea-shop verbal clashes occurred. 'Down-river people' became words of derision, while the refugees were known to speak openly, as well as to themselves, of *Chwan hao-dze* – Szechwan rats. Yet despite points of friction there was much mutual learning, and it was never questioned but that all people, whether local or from other parts, were determined, whatever the cost, to resist Japanese aggression.

Bao Hsin-min always told me the latest rumours from the tea-shop in the Lane. 'They say the Generalissimo's own troops are no longer fighting, but are holding off,' he said one day. 'They are making our Szechwanese men do all the fighting.' Among the students, however, there was another version of the story. Friction had devloped in high places and the united front, which had been effective since the General-issimo had been captured in 1936, was weakening. The Eighth Route Army soldiers, under Mao Tse-tung and Chu Deh, were relentlessly continuing their guerilla warfare, but no longer did the National Government co-operate with them. In fact, it was rumoured, military supplies were being cut off and some of Chiang Kai-shek's own troops were removed from fighting against Japan in order to keep watch over the Red Armies in the north.

Political and military events were of great concern to me just then. Mary and our three children, Djieh-djieh, Mei-mei and little Di-di (whom I had seen only as a baby when I was last on leave), were now in America, delaying their journey to China. It seemed certain that eventually the war in Europe would spread, and Mary and I were both anxious that we should face it together, for once the war extended it would be more difficult to be reunited.

I went to seek Molly's advice. On the way there I met Wu Deh-chin, who might, I thought, know more about the actual political situation. She too had heard many rumours, but knew nothing definite. 'Of course everyone knows the

Japanese must be defeated,' she told me. 'The communists believe that the only effective way to do this is to have a social revolution now. The people then will fight as free men and women and not as conscripted slaves. Old Chiang, however, says let us fight the Japanese first, and then have a social revolution afterwards. That means: never. The people will remain poor, downtrodden, and the landlords continue to be rich and powerful.'

'We must wait and then we shall see,' Deh-chin had finally advised, in words used by many much wiser than she. 'When your eyes are open there are many things which are different from what they appear to be on the surface.' She turned and left me, walking without looking back. Above the blue collar of her cotton gown there was a triangle of skin, exposed by the parting of her plaits – so white in contrast with the intense blackness of her hair. Did this Chinese girl really possess eyes that truly saw, and ears which heard?

In her landlord's courtyards, as I passed through on the way to Molly's home beyond, all was bustle. Now that the summer was come they had hired for the day the old man who fluffs cotton with his bow. Women, on the paths round the yard, were ripping up old quilts and opening padded winter garments, now thin and hard with use. Some of the cotton filling had been washed and was drying in the sunshine. Together with new cotton, it was being transformed into soft billowing down to fill the covers once again, making them fat and warm, ready for winter when it came. Over the noise of chatter was the rhythmic twanging of the wire, held taut, as the old man struck with his mallet, causing the cotton to fluff up, caught in the vibrating wire. I stood to watch him as he worked so skilfully and, it seemed, so easily.

'What is your honourable country?' He politely acknowledged my presence. When I told him, he asked: 'Do you know that Japan and my China are at war?' His face was

turned to me, but he never ceased his work. He would not believe that high-nosed foreign devils could truly be aware of Chinese affairs. Probably, if he thought of us at all, he dismissed us along with other powerful exploiters, landlords and officials, with whom we westerners so often mixed. He certainly had no idea that my country was at war in Europe and also might soon be fighting Japan – and Mary was still on the far side of the Pacific Ocean.

Molly agreed that it was right to urge Mary to come back to China as soon as she could get a passage – which was, we knew, what Mary herself wanted. We believed that in a world at war, Duliang would be as safe a place for children as any. China had taught us that personal security was not the most important gift life had to offer. Any doubts which may have remained in my own mind were dispelled by Molly's avowal: 'It is not good for families to be separated for too long a time. Children should have two parents.' On the way home I called at the post office and with Bao's help sent a cable to Mary suggesting she came as soon as possible.

A week later, I saw the stout figure of Bao Hsin-min coming towards my home on the campus. He was in a long Chinese gown, which was only half fastened. He was hot with hurry. When he saw me his face broke into smiles. 'They are coming – your dear little children – at the beginning of December.' The reply to my cable had come and friendship demanded that he himself should deliver it. 'It is good news for you,' he declared as he handed me the carefully sealed envelope. It was good news indeed. Yet I was anxious lest they should be too late.

A few days before I was due to leave for Hong Kong to meet my family, I went to say goodbye to Yü Tse-tan. He was painting, but I was happy to see that people were beginning to appear once more among the rocks and plants. Yet they were not the people of the Lane, of modern China: they were from the distant past. He had returned to the Golden Age, when sages walked amid the 'mountains and waters', instructing their disciples with the wisdom which has guided all those who since their days have dwelt 'within the four seas'. In delicate pastel shades, under gnarled trees, these philosophers walked, sipped their tea, studied or wrote. Their scanty beards and delicate moustaches were lovingly painted, hair by hair. On their heads was the gear of bygone dynasties, and in their hands strange twisted sticks. In gardens or temple groves they were surrounded by the symbols of flower and fruit, bat and bird. Was Yü trying to say that old China had a message for today, that the ageless spirit of the 'People under Heaven' was immortal, not to be destroyed? As I turned over the pictures, charmed by their beauty, I wondered if the dream had lasted through too many centuries and the awakening too rude, the change too sudden for these precious things to have significance today. Yet, as happened when I was with Yü, I felt my own anxiety fading, for I knew that the artist himself had hope.

It was raining when I was with him; and as he bade me

'walk slowly' and 'travel in peace' the shower was not over. He would have had me remain longer. 'It will pass – rain does not fall for ever,' I assured him as I left, still thinking of his picture of Nanking, hanging in his room: the storm bending the willows, and the dark rain lashing the surface of the lake.

In Wheelbarrow Lane, the seller of dog-skin plasters was sheltering against a wall with his little cart beside him. He was in his summer gown of patched and faded blue. The rain dripped from his small hat of plaited leaves, but round his shoulders a cape of palm fibre gave him protection.

'You are wet with rain,' I said as I passed. 'Sold any plasters?'

He ignored my question. A happy smile of the cheery optimism felt by even the poorest on the Lane, lit up his face. 'Look, Hsien-sen,' he pointed with his chin towards the sky, 'there is a rainbow eating the rain.'

XI

Farewell

———◇———

MY BREAKFAST was finished. Only two more and I should be leaving for Hong Kong, I realised, as I rang the little bell which Mrs Fu always put by my plate. When she came in from the kitchen, she said, 'He would like to see you.'

She rarely mentioned her husband by name. As a modest wife when she wanted to speak to him, even in his presence, she would say to her son, if he were there: 'Tell your father I'm going on the street. Ask him if there is anything he needs.'

'I'll come,' I told her, although the Chinese meant 'I've as good as arrived already'. When I got to the little room I knew that Fu Lu-chin was seriously ill. There was a glimmer in his eyes when he saw me, and his lips moved. 'Hsien-sen,' I imagined was what he whispered.

'Don't worry, it's all right now.' I took his hand, but the light was fading from his eyes, although he continued to look at me.

'Now he can die,' said Mrs Fu without emotion. 'He woke early and wanted you. He wouldn't die until he had seen you. Before it was light he asked: "Where is Hsien-sen?" I told him: "He hasn't got up yet." Then later he asked again: "Where is Hsien-sen?" I replied: "He is eating." "Ask him," he said.'

'And you mean to say you let me eat my breakfast and never told me.' I was angry.

'Old Fu was always a nuisance. *Gai-se-ha,* wasn't he?' She defended herself inconsequentially. Her words were harsh, but were affectionately spoken. Even now she would not speak to him directly, although it is doubtful if he would have understood.

I sent her off with a note to the doctor; and, as she was fingering her basket, anxious to do her shopping, I told her I would stay by Fu's side until her return.

When the doctor arrived, a western woman recently come to China, she confirmed that there was nothing to be done. She suggested Cook Fu should be taken to the Jen Dah hospital, but I knew how he feared all such foreign places. It was his right peacefully to die at his home.

It is said that people in their last moments review their lives: certainly during the two hours of waiting I looked back over the years Fu Lu-chin had been with us, how he had served us, loved by our children, part of our lives. Sometimes he amused us, at others we felt exasperation; often he filled us with admiration, and occasionally drew forth our pity – for eight full years, his life was a strand inextricably interwoven with ours. When his breathing changed, and then quietly stopped, we had indeed lost a friend.

A few minutes later his wife returned, accompanied by Mrs Bao, her old neighbour, to whom she had naturally turned at this time. Together the two women whisked Old Fu from the bed and laid him on some boards, supported on two trestle stools which, had I but noticed, were placed ready for him. Mrs Fu had spent the morning not only doing trivial shopping for me, but had purchased grave clothes for her husband.

News rapidly spread, and before long other members of the informal Jen Dah cooks' union began to gather round. Three of them went to buy a coffin, the last gift I could offer. It took four men to bring it back, it was so large and heavy. 'Good, good,' said the cooks, while two of them lifted the lid, exaggerating its weight to honour the dead. 'A hundred catties at least.' Black lacquered, shining, every square inch was examined with care. Then they placed the coffin on trestles so that it stood at the edge of the garden, outside Fu's room, in the shelter of the broad eaves.

Sawdust was sprinkled to make a thick layer at the bottom. Above that they spread a bed of soft cypress sprays, neighbours and friends joining in stripping the branches with their hands. When all was smooth and even, they carried out Fu Lu-chin, who had been made ready by the women, and placed him in the middle, a pillow under his head. There was no haste in this, for it was of greatest importance that he should be centred with exactness. They moved him here, then there, just a fraction up or down, to this side or that, until everyone present was satisfied that his position couldn't be bettered. Then they wedged him securely, with bundles of cypress leaves rolled in cloth; and because he was short and the coffin long, they rested his feet on a cushion made of grey tiles.

The cloth which had covered his face was removed. He looked very thin, the cheeks shrunken, skin brown like old wrinkled parchment, but the tufts of hair from his nostrils sprouted more bravely than ever, now sadly untwisted. He was still wearing his old round brimless black hat, but on his feet were shoes such as are seen in old Chinese paintings, and his dress was that of ancient days. In the world of spirits he would not feel out of place – he was clad in clothes such as were worn by the puppets in the last scene of the Tiger Story, which we had watched with such pleasure at the wedding of banker Hsiung Wei-lin and Ruby.

Mrs Bao felt responsible for the widow, as she had matched her with Cook Fu. She told again how it had come about, perhaps in order to make clear her claims, as the widow was afraid lest the first wife should return from the country to demand Fu's meagre goods. There were other fears also. Fu, it seemed, had been afraid to die, and his widow was anxious lest he should not rest in peace. It was commonly said on the Lane that foreigners, who in those days were felt to have special wisdom, believed that unless water was sprinkled upon him by a priest, a man would find after death no rest but only torment. I assured them that my Quaker parents had never received the ritual water, their lives had been good, and I had no anxiety for them now they were dead. This filial testimony was, I hoped, some assurance for them; but it was sad that Fu should have been burdened by a new misunderstood fear from the West, when the Chinese themselves already had more than enough with which to cope.

To keep Fu warm a narrow quilt was tucked round him, and over his face tobacco leaves were spread, to prevent the escape through his pale lips of the diseases and weaknesses from which he had died, and which unless imprisoned might affect others. Then all helped to raise the heavy lid and carefully placed it very slightly askew. Mrs Fu, drawing near, in a loud voice, so that all could hear, called to her husband: 'Fu Lu-chin, Fu Lu-chin, I have treated you well – as well as I am able. You cannot be offended by me. Fu Lu-chin, do you hear?' Then she started to wail, and continued until it was time to prepare my supper. Then she wailed again.

Next morning, their breakfast chores completed, Fu's fellow cooks again drifted towards my home. Mrs Bao, some of her children with her, soon joined them. Mrs Fu tore into small pieces some red ribbon she had bought. 'Wear a little red, for helping us,' she thanked me as she handed me a piece. To the others she said much more simply: 'To keep off evil spirits.'

The rest of the day was a wake. The coffin was moved out into the garden and a square table placed astride it. On this was set an enlarged photograph of Fu – the tufts from his nostrils were the dominant feature. Symetrically arranged on the table were pairs of vases of flowers, candles, plates of red persimmons, biscuits and coloured rice-flour candy. The mourners sat around gossiping and drinking tea, while several of the cooks started to prepare the feast. The work was interrupted when they trooped to their homes to cook their employers' midday meals; but they quickly returned and all was ready by late afternoon.

Halfway through the meal we were summoned again to the coffin: the *chi-djiang*, the painter, had come. The table was moved and the great lid lifted off. The tobacco leaves were raised and each guest was invited to look his last on Old Fu. With so many witnesses there could be no doubt that it was he who lay firmly fixed in that great wooden 'house'.

The lid was replaced with exactness and care, then sealed by the painter and lacquered to make it all air-tight. Once again it was time for Mrs Fu to wail and chant in sing-song lament, telling forth her distress at the loss of her man, as the painter gave the final touch with his cloth of varnish, down one side of the coffin, and then up the other. When he reached the top his work was completed. 'Enough, enough,' cried the chorus of cooks, and Mrs Fu became silent. We resumed our meal.

Next day I had to leave before the coffin was carried to the grave. My air passage was already booked to Chungking, from there to connect with the plane to Hong Kong, flying by night over the Japanese lines. I dare not postpone my journey for seats were difficult to obtain and my family was due to arrive in less than a week.

'He was always a nuisance,' repeated Mrs Fu when I said goodbye to her. 'Dying just at this time, and then choosing to be buried on a day so inconvenient for you.' She was going to buy paper money and incense to burn at the grave: 'To open the way and make it easy for him.'

During my plane journey away from Duliang my thoughts naturally turned again to the people I had left, my colleagues and students at Jen Dah, but especially to the

People of the Lane – to Bao Hsin-min, his wife and family, also to Hsiung Wei-lin and Ruby, who had recently slipped so much into the background as happens, even to closest friends, in a country where communications are poor, and letter writing not a habit. I pondered the philosophy of Artist Yü, and thought with admiration of Molly in her marriage with Deh-min; but mainly it was Cook Fu who was present in my mind.

I could imagine with haunting detail the little procession. Eight men, yoked four at each end, carrying their heavy burden slung on stout ropes along the uneven tracks to the burial place in the country. Before the coffin there would be the small group of mourners, chief among them Mrs Fu and her son, now a student at Jen Chung, the Middle School. They would be wearing unbleached sackcloth, with hoods over their heads. Representatives of the cooks would be there, and Mrs Bao. Molly had said that naturally she would go too: it was for her Fu had worked before he had come to us. Deh-min had his classes and probably could not walk with the others.

On my journey I had no profound reflections which I can share to conclude this glimpse into the lives of my friends. It was my expectation that I should be among them once again in less than a fortnight. I was much more concerned with the prospect of being with Mary again, and seeing our children, the youngest of whom I hardly knew. I had, I remember, a deep sense of gratitude to Molly who, despite her own busy life, was to help Mrs Fu get ready the house at Jen Dah. The prospect was deeply stirring . . . .

A few hours after our family reunion (a desperately fortuitous affair so it happened) bombs fell on Pearl Harbour and on Hong Kong. Eventually, captured by the Japanese, we had years of internment, living in poverty, with inadequate food and clothing, lacking privilege, forced to obey the whim of those who had power, condemned to watch our own children suffer – experiences common enough for those who lived in Wheelbarrow Lane. We discovered the bitterness of a way of life which Wu Deh-chin had believed no foreigner could ever know, least of all a relatively rich and secure teacher from over the ocean.

From behind the barbed wire we could only imagine the anxiety of the final years of their long war which our friends on the Lane were facing, the galloping inflation, the demoralization, all of which were eventually to lead to the acceptance of a new pattern of life. Yet, as we thought of them, it was no longer as mere observers. Our own privations gave us fresh insight into their lives and an understanding of the humble philosophy with which they faced life's sorrows and joys.

When I was leaving Jen Dah my senior chemistry students had handed me a *Departing Poem of Separation*. It remained in my pocket. Japanese guards seized it, but read it with some pleasant appreciation of the words addressed to a teacher. They handed it back, doubtless knowing it was harmless. Yet it did in fact contain a hidden secret message for me. Beyond the sorrow that I had unwillingly deserted my students, there remained the warmth of knowing that I was in some measure accepted and wanted. Below the compact lines of characters, the students had written an English translation:

We feel harsh winds blowing, tears shedding, hearts mournful.
Our thoughts follow the feet of your fast receding steed.
The song of the oriole comforts the spirits of those you have left.
Willows are waving, deep-rooted, green. We pluck a branch.
It is for you from your pupils with the blessing of Heaven.
Return to us, like the martin which flies to the East.